TEST YOUR OWN
MENTAL HEALTH:
A Self-Evaluation Workbook
and Self-Cure Programme

form Thomas
for Papa

TEST YOUR OWN MENTAL HEALTH

A Self-Evaluation Workbook and Self-Cure Programme

by

William Gladstone

PAPERFRONTS
ELLIOT RIGHT WAY BOOKS
KINGSWOOD, SURREY, U.K.

Made and printed in Great Britain by
C. Nicholls & Company Ltd.,
The Philips Park Press, Manchester.

CONTENTS

ABOUT THE AUTHOR

William Gladstone graduated from Yale College *Honores meritis clarissimis* and holds graduate degrees from the University of Salamanca and Harvard University. He is a member of the American Anthropological Association, an author of technical books on medicine and property, and has served as researcher for a documentary special network television. Under the auspices of a grant from the National Institute of Mental Health, Mr. Gladstone carried out behavioural research in the United States, Spain, and Brazil. He has taught at Phillips Academy Andover and Harvard University.

ACKNOWLEDGEMENT

The author would like to acknowledge the work of psychologist Dr. Douglas H. Powell of Harvard University and his kind permission to allow the publication of this book. The diagnostic chart and theory of Five Stages of adaptability were developed by Dr. Powell in conjunction with his research as a N.A.S.A. (National Aeronautics and Space Administration) consultant and Harvard University affiliated psychologist.

The test has been reprinted in the NEW YORK POST, the NATIONAL STAR, the PHILADELPHIA BULLETIN, the BOSTON HERALD AMERICAN. It has been demonstrated on numerous television and radio shows throughout the United States.

The diagnostic chart and the concept of five stages of mental health are part of a general theory of personality and normal behaviour which Dr. Powell will publish in a forthcoming book.

TEST YOUR OWN MENTAL HEALTH: A SELF-EVALUATION WORKBOOK AND SELF-CURE PROGRAMME is, however, entirely the responsibility of the author. I have adapted Dr. Powell's chart to the needs of the general public and have developed my own thoughts concerning the nature and treatment of mental illness. I have also given my own interpretation to Dr. Powell's chart and relied upon my background as a professional anthropologist in the presentation of symptoms and definitions that are not necessarily in agreement with Dr. Powell's own views.

INTRODUCTION

This book is a guide toward understanding and dealing with stress and mental illness. It offers a programme for viewing mental health and illness as a five-stage process in which specific characteristics of thought and behaviour can be isolated and interrelated in a concrete framework. This programme enables the reader to make a judgment about his or her own mental health. Obviously the same framework and scale of stages can be used to infer the general state of mental health and stability of close friends and family.

Great caution must be taken, however, if this book is to be used as a guide toward testing or measuring the mental health of others. As will be shown by a discussion of the traits and stages used in measuring mental health, single characteristics and even groups of traits taken out of context do not necessarily imply a specific stage of mental health or illness. Only by viewing the individual as a whole and taking into account as many aspects of his life-situation as possible can the framework for testing mental health introduced in this book be used effectively. In general, this information about particulars of one's life-situation, including the knowledge of one's inner thoughts, is not available to outsiders but only to the individual himself. It is for this reason that this book is primarily intended as a guide toward testing your *own* mental health and not that of friends and certainly not that of casual acquaintances.

This book is intended as a guide toward a general assessment of your mental health. Do not expect to precisely diagnose yourself as suffering from manic depression (extreme bouts of depression), mild

9

psychosis (mental disorder), or as being perfectly well-adjusted. Such precise formulations can be worked out only through contacts with psychologists, guidance counsellors, or others with specific training in clinical psychology. Judicious use of the stages, conceptual framework, behavioural characteristics, and other information provided in this book should indicate to you if the problems you are dealing with, and the styles you have evolved for dealing with them, are adequate responses to normal stress or indicate deeper stresses, or inappropriate coping styles which could usefully be discussed with a professional.

Recent research indicates that fewer than one out of four persons in the United States of America suffering from mental illness receive any form of professional medical therapy. Part of the reason for this is the unavailability and/or high expense of medical therapy in the United States. The position in Great Britain and other parts of the world is similar. Another reason is that many persons do receive some form of therapy from friends, clergy, colleagues, healers, and others which is not strictly "professional". This book is intended to foster greater use of these non-professional sources of therapy as well as to increase communication between non-professionals and clinical psychologists. A careful reading of the descriptions of mental stages should alert non-professionals to the danger signals of personal breakdown and warn them when the symptoms of their "patients" exceed their experience and ability to help and suggest calling for additional professional therapeutic aid. Again this is not suggesting that this book offers a formula or can serve as an instant diagnostic device. However, without serving as a magical instrument of diagnosis and a substitute for medical and psychological training, this book does presume to enable you to make the best use of your common sense to note and respond to danger signals in your own behaviour and that of close friends and loved ones.

1

HOW TO USE THIS BOOK

The core of this book is a table of Five Stages of Adaptability developed by psychologist Douglas H. Powell of Harvard University. This table consists of seven areas of behaviour referred to as characteristics and related to each one the expected behaviour corresponding to each of the five general stages of adaptability or mental health.

Definitions are provided for all significant terms and examples, and general discussions of each area of behaviour are included as well. Once familiar with the nature of the characteristics judged as significant indicators of mental health, you are ready to test your own mental health. First look at the specific behaviour patterns associated with the seven characteristics which define each stage. Next go through the presentation of the five stages of adaptability, checking to be sure you understand the significance of each. Later you will tick off those behaviour patterns which most clearly resemble your own. You should not be surprised if some of your behaviour falls into each of the five stages of adaptability. A single psychotic (disturbed) trait does not a psychotic make. However, if a large number of neurotic characteristics have been ticked off in your self-appraisal, you may be able to profit from some form of psychotherapy. Given the loose and subjective nature of this self-test for mental health you are advised to check through the characteristics on at least two different occasions, corresponding to two different moods (a second set of diagnostic checklists and Self-Evaluation Chart is included for this, from page 171). If this second, and subsequent re-appraisals still indicate that much of your behaviour pattern falls into stages three, four, and five, refer to the later sections of this book — Where Do You Go When You're in Trouble?, Philosophy of Mental Health, Treatment, and the Self-Cure Programme.

2

DEFINITIONS

ADAPTABILITY

Adaptability — the ability to adapt — is the key to survival of all species of plants and animals, including man. Darwin's breakthrough in the biological sciences was to observe that only those species survived that were able to adapt to changes in their environment. Many animals that were overdependent upon a specific behaviour pattern or a specific physical characteristic — for example large sized, peculiarly-shaped claws, evolved for the hunting of particular animals or the consumption of particular plants — were unable to survive dramatic changes in climate, extinction of those plants or animals, or the competition of other species. They were unable to adapt to changing conditions and, thus, were doomed to extinction themselves. These changes were brought about both by the species itself (as in the case of overhunting), or by exterior conditions (an ice age causing dramatic changes in climate and the corresponding fauna and plant life which had sustained them), or by other competitors or predators moving in from other territories.

It has been argued that man has survived and come to dominate the planet precisely because he has remained the most adaptable of all animal species, specializing in a nonspecialized organ — the brain. The argument of this book is that, as with the human species, so with human individuals. Just as Darwin explained that the health of the species lay in its ability to preserve its adaptability to changing conditions, so we suggest that individual health can be viewed in terms of the individual's ability to adapt to the changing world about him and the changes that are encountered in the normal interactions and activities of everyday life.

In putting forward adaptability as the goal and measure of mental health, we are not imposing an *a priori* (above all else) value upon human life. Adaptability is a culture-bound concept. Behaviour that may have been defined as adaptable 50 years ago may not hold true today, any more than a contemporary British definition would hold true in China or other parts of the world. Each culture or time period creates different modes of adaptability. Nonetheless, for each culture the ability of the individual to adapt to the culture can usefully be understood as a measure of mental health. This holds true for subgroups within a given culture as well and transcends differences in values, religion, politics, or morals.

In human terms we are using adaptability and mental health to imply the ability to work, love, and play in balanced measure. This definition is taken from Aristotle and from the Greeks. There are cultures in which the behaviours associated with work, love, and play are far different than in our own culture. But to our knowledge there is no society which does not value the ability to engage in work, love, and play activities. Indeed, from a biological viewpoint, such activities are prerequisites to the continued existence of any human group (activities of production, reproduction, and recuperation).

What is normal adaptability will change from culture to culture and perhaps within cultures from generation to generation and social class to social class. It will also vary from individual to individual within any sociological category. Normal adaptability can be thought of as living up to one's potential and does not imply preconceived notions of what one individual's potential is, as opposed to another's, or that an objective standard need exist. The one constant in our view of normal adaptability is the notion of inner harmony. Only when a man is at peace with himself can his energies be directed toward adapting to his outside world and not merely to himself.

The converse of our definition of mental health as normal adaptability is the notion of mental illness as ever more restricted patterns of adaptation ending ultimately in the inability to adapt at all, or in death. An individual tormented by inner chaos and conflicts is unable to lend his full energies toward adapting to other persons and events in the world around him. He must choose specialized patterns of interacting with others which do not demand tapping his already over-extended resources. He is unlikely to adopt new response patterns and will be more likely to settle for dogmatic and rigid patterns of interaction with himself and others which will not test nor tax his limited adaptability.

A fuller view of the notion of adaptability as a measure of mental health will be drawn out in the more specific discussions of particular stages of adaptability. The important point we have tried to establish thus far is that adaptability is an appropriate concept for viewing stages of mental health.

The most important contribution of this way of viewing mental health is that adaptability can be measured and, consequently, so can mental health. As will be seen in the discussion that follows, the abstract notion of adaptability can be broken down to seven concrete and observable characteristics. Taken as a whole these seven characteristics generate a concrete picture of five distinct stages of human adaptability by which individuals can be distinguished and against which their behaviour can be measured.

CHARACTERISTICS

The characteristics upon which this model of stages of adaptability as stages of mental health is based are (1) Tension, (2) Mood, (3) Thought, (4) Activity, (5)

Organization/Control, (6) Interpersonal, and (7) Physical. Each characteristic refers to a definable area of behaviour which is separate, observable and autonomous. These are seven characteristics which clinical psychologists have found to be useful categories or working hypotheses in evaluating and predicting human behaviour. In actual life there is great interaction among these seven characteristics with changes and states in one characteristic often associated with, and sometimes dependent upon, states and changes in other characteristics. For example, a change in characteristic 2, Mood, might either provoke, or be the result of, a change in a love relationship (no. 6, Interpersonal). For precisely this reason, these seven characteristics, when taken together, serve as an accurate measure and method for evaluating an individual's stage of adaptability or mental health. The five stages of adaptability which Dr. Powell has isolated — (I) Normal Adaptability, (II) Emergency Regulatory Behaviour, (III) Neurotic Coping Styles, (IV) Neurotic Characters, and (V) Psychotic (disturbed) Behaviour and Conduct Disorders — are defined by isolating patterns of behaviour for each of the seven characteristics which, when taken together, indicate general levels of mental fitness.

The different characteristics can be likened to different kinds of evidence in a legal case or mystery story. A single piece of apparently incriminating evidence, such as motive, is not necessarily significant unless associated with other types of evidence — access to the murder weapon, lack of an alibi, opportunity to perform the act, etc. When several different strands of evidence are taken together and complement each other, then and only then is a strong case made for reaching a conclusion.

The same holds true for looking at the different behaviour patterns associated with each of the seven characteristics. A single psychotic behaviour pattern for characteristic 7, Physical, associated with a majority of normal adaptability and emergency regulatory behaviour would not necessarily indicate psychosis (mental disorder) or even any major mental problems. Psychotic behaviour patterns for all seven characteristics, however, would be a practically unshakable indication that a psychosis or other major conduct disorder is in fact present.

Do not assume that you understand exactly what the various characteristics mean. They are everyday words but they are being used with greater precision in order to distinguish carefully and categorize behaviour unambiguously. As such, they take on a more specific clinical meaning, not at odds with everyday use but certainly more restricted. Glance over the following definitions and examples of behaviour for each of the seven characteristics.

Characteristic 1: Tension

Tension refers to the level and impact of anxiety. Signs of tension include agitation, fingernail-biting, sweating, rapid breathing, and tightness. The famous tension-headache commercials might be cases of the characteristic of tension as used in this book, but most cases include other dimensions such as irritability and physical manifesations of tension which are properly categorized as relating to characteristics 2, Mood, and 7, Physical.

A certain amount of anxiety or tension in everyday life is both unavoidable and necessary. Not to feel nervous or tense at all on a first date, when attending an important business conference, or upon delivering a school address is uncommon and not necessarily desirable. In fact, for many tasks tension plays a vital role which contributes to and improves performance. A common example is the tension and excitement an athlete or musician may feel just before the start of an athletic contest, or a performance. These cases, depending upon degree and intensity, would be normal instances of tension. What would be abnormal would be such an intense degree of tension that an individual could not perform at all, as in the case of a performer's stage fright or of a young business executive's getting so keyed up before a conference that he is unable to effectively present his thoughts and suggestions in a coherent manner.

Since the cause of tension is an integral component in evaluating the positive or negative aspects of tension as a measure of adaptability, characteristic 1, Tension, will also be used to refer to the cause of tension in the presentation of stages of adaptability.

Characteristic 2: Mood

Mood is how a person feels. Everyone experiences different moods at different times. There are moods of happiness, sadness, optimism, pessimism, or just feeling numb. There are irritable moods and pleasant moods. Even a grumpy, irritable boss who never seems to be pleasant may have moods of lesser irritability. As such, a mood is a relative term which depends in large part on general personality type. What is an optimistic mood for a cynic may resemble a pessimistic mood for a wide-eyed idealist.

In evaluating mood, it is best to judge by your own experience of emotions and not by stereotyped images of joy or sadness as presented in films and television.

Nevertheless, there are objective criteria for evaluating changes in mood and the influence of mood upon character as a measure of mental health. Normally, moods have a direct cause and are of short or moderate duration. A failure on an examination, not getting an expected rise at work, losing a football game after making a crucial error — these are the kind of events that provoke moods of sadness, irritability, or depression, depending upon individual variations. This is to be expected, and quite intense moods might result. What would be abnormal is such events creating a depressed mood that endured days, or even weeks, and which was not in accordance with more positive experiences after the initial disappointment. In cases of severe mental disorder, a mood of depression or numbness may so overwhelm an individual that he is incapable of responding to his environment at all.

A good guide toward evaluating your patterning and experience of moods is to look at your sense of humour. A person who is not suffering from mental problems does not lose his sense of humour for long, even in the midst of intense feelings of anger, frustration, or sadness. He is able to step back and laugh at himself and not take his life so seriously. A person with a good sense of humour is also able to appreciate the feelings of others and to allow them, through jokes and other affectionately-intended overtures, to draw him out of his sadness or anger.

Loss of sense of humour or an intense patterning of humour, more in the direction of a permanent hostile wit which manifests itself with biting sarcasm, both in reference to others and oneself, is an indication that, at least in the area of mood experiences, an individual is suffering from some form of mental stress. Total loss of sense of humour or the inability to take anything lightly or playfully is associated with more severe mental disorders.

Characteristic 3: Thought

The behaviour category of Thought refers to what a person thinks about. There are different ways of classifying thought behaviour, including notions of mature thought as opposed to regressive, appropriate as opposed to inappropriate, and continuous as opposed to periodic thoughts.

An example of inappropriate thought would be for a

student during an examination to be unable to stop thinking about the pretty legs of his teacher throughout the entire examination. Periodic thoughts are those that recur at intervals but which are interrupted by other thoughts. Continuous thinking is the ability to start a line of reasoning and to bring it to a conclusion without other thoughts interfering. Regressive thoughts refer mostly to fantasies about past situations that are not in touch with present circumstances. Mature thoughts are those which take account of yourself and the world as it is and relate them to positive action.

A danger signal pointing to a breakdown in thought behaviour is apparent when thoughts are no longer related to concrete events and do not lead to action. A common initial phase of such a breakdown is circular worrying. A certain amount of this is probably inevitable and in its mildest form resembles double or triple checking shopping lists or the car before making a trip. But more severe circular worrying is obvious when someone thinks about all the things that could possibly go wrong without being able to relate the worry to any form of constructive action. An example would be someone before a job interview who started to worry like this: "The interviewer won't like me. He probably saw me fumble the ball in the big game last year. The sun will shine in my eyes and I'll have to squint and look stupid. He'll get a phone call during the interview and I won't know what to do. I'll start to sweat. He probably knows that my brother was just sacked. If he saw the game last year I'm finished for sure. He probably doesn't like Catholics," etc.

Such circular worrying before a stressful event, such as a job interview, though unproductive, is not necessarily particularly abnormal. Worrying in this fashion about many, or most, events in one's life would be. This kind of thinking leads to the inability to make decisions, which is a sign of more severe mental disorder. In extreme cases, obsessive thoughts and gross perceptual distortions totally isolate one's thinking from the everyday world and are sure signs that an individual is under intensive mental stress.

A word of caution in evaluating thought behaviour: most people at some time in their lives experience all the forms of thought behaviour, even those associated with stages four and five. The key to evaluating your level of thought behaviour is to focus on your most common patterns, not the occasional exceptions.

Characteristic 4: Activity

Activity is what a person is interested in, and does. Activity includes work, play, hobbies, and any task or project which engages both mind and body. The kind and nature of activity in which you engage is related to your energy level. When your energy level is low you are less likely to engage in new activities and more likely to feel fatigue or exhaustion rather than enthusiasm or satisfied expended energy at the end of an activity.

The activity of a healthy person is characterized by an interest in different kinds of activity and a sense of competence in many areas of both personal and group activities. The ability to take risks, to be mediocre in some areas, and to try again after failing is characteristic of a healthy patterning of activities. Under normal circumstances, an individual is able to engage in both continuous activities, such as working on an assembly line for several hours without stopping, and in uneven activities, such as preparing a meal in which you might be called upon to add spices to a stew at different intervals and change temperatures, while playing a game of bridge with friends.

When activity becomes compulsive or ritualistic — that is, when you exercise because it is good for you or play cards because you promised the lads but are detached from the activity and not really a part of it — then something is wrong. Notions such as just going through the motions or feeling only relief and no satisfaction when the day's activities are over — "Well, I got through another day" — are signs of mental stress.

Some key areas to focus on in evaluating your activity behaviour are in the rhythm of your life: are you often hyperactive without really accomplishing anything? Do you do only things which are "important", never taking time off to do nothing or something silly or inconsequential? *Never* to engage in anything frivolous is a key error. Do you follow a rigid set of activities with infrequent changes?

Characteristic 5: Organization/Control

Organization/control is essentially self-discipline. It refers to the capacity and freedom to plan and carry out what one wishes to do. Organization/control behaviour affects both work and play and manifests itself in a variety of ways.

The most common indicators are how you organize the major activities of your life. Do you take on and finish tasks on schedule without difficulty? Or do you overextend your abilities in an attempt to do more than you comfortably can in the time at your disposal? Do you need constant encouragement from others to keep at a difficult or tedious job or are you able to set your own pace and provide your own motivation and self-discipline? Do you need a perfect work environment or are you able to handle ambiguity and disturbances without becoming unsettled? Do you learn from experience or act impulsively, not really examining the pros and cons of different problem-solving strategies?

In evaluating your organization/control behaviour, a key measure is to see how you handle unexpected and unpredictable events. It is normal to experience some anxiety and frustration when things don't turn out as expected — a parade prevents you from going home from work the usual way, someone gets sick and you are forced to take on greater responsibility at home or at work, you plan an outdoor barbecue and it rains, etc. The important measure is how you behave in these circumstances. Do you go into a rage, cursing the parade, fellow occupants in the car, and your wife when you get home, or do you just curse the parade and your bad luck and don't start yelling at everyone in sight? When it rains at the barbecue are you able to set up an alternative plan in the house and maintain the pleasant spirit of the party, or do you get depressed and wish your guests would go home and leave you alone to suffer your rotten luck. These are minor cases but are indicators of the kinds of situations which enable you to judge your level of self-control and your ability to control your internal feelings. It's easy to be a considerate and loving spouse when you feel like a million but it's how you behave when you feel rotten that indicates your organization/control behaviour.

Characteristic 6: Interpersonal

The interpersonal characteristic refers to the style and stability of relations with parents, colleagues, fellow workers, neighbours, friends, and others. Are your relations intimate or superficial? Do you have a range of different kinds of relationships? Can you *be* a friend as well as *have* friends? Do you always insist on getting your own way? Are you overly anxious about pleasing others? Or are you able to have a real interchange with others in which you experience a variety of roles and feelings at different times as circumstances vary?

Some key areas to watch in terms of interpersonal behaviour are whether or not you bear grudges, or pattern your relationships along strict lines of dependence or manipulation. Any overly rigid pattern is an indication that you are responding with only part of your personality toward others. If you mould all your relationships along predetermined lines, it is an indication that you are not really responding to others but are reacting against inner conflicts in ways that may have been appropriate in the past or with a specific relative or close friend. People are different and your relationships with people should reflect these differences. If all your relationships with others are of the same general type, you are both giving and calling upon a limited aspect of your own personality and the personalities of others.

If your relationships with others are characterized by destructive patterns with grudges arising out of misunderstandings of a repetitive nature, you could probably use some help. A good indicator to keep an eye on in this respect is the relative stability of your relationships. Are you engaged in long-term, stable relationships or is your life characterized by short-term, up-and-down relationships of an ambiguous variety?

Characteristic 7: Physical

Physical behaviour is perhaps that most overlooked by people in assessing their mental health. Research has demonstrated that many mental diseases are closely linked to physical symptoms. Stress has been shown to alter the production of hormones and chemicals in the body, leading to a variety of symptoms.

In this book, physical behaviour refers not only to how well a person feels but also to the presence or absence of bodily symptoms. Common areas in which mental problems may manifest themselves include fluctuations in eating and sleeping patterns, gastrointestinal disorders, skin blemishes, headache, insomnia, and drug and alcohol abuse or addiction.

Many of these disorders may have causes unrelated to mental stress but their existence can contribute to heightening existing mental problems and provoking new difficulties. Of course, there are many cases of gastrointestinal problems (wind, heartburn, constipation, diarrhoea, etc.) and headaches which are temporary problems created by eating too much or the wrong foods. However, these same symptoms, if they recur over a long period of time, can be indications of mental, or possibly physical ailments, as well.

One further note: When we say that a physical symptom, such as a pain in the chest or the back, may be a manifestation of a mental problem or of mental stress, this does not imply that the physical pain is not real and disturbing; nor does it imply that the physical pain itself should not be treated, as well.

3

THEORY OF FIVE STAGES OF MENTAL HEALTH

The idea of looking at mental health in terms of stages has been gaining acceptance, both in research and clinical psychology. There is a degree of arbitrariness in defining separate stages of mental health. This is unavoidable in the creation and use of scientific categories in all social sciences and many areas of the natural sciences as well. Nonetheless, in an area of such delicacy and popular misconception as mental illness, one must be careful to point out that all categories, including the ones used in this book, are relative and depend on circumstances. There is no such thing as a normal person, a neurotic person, or a schizophrenic who exactly fits the medical definition. These labels reflect working hypotheses. Knowledge of the strict medical definitions is not important for the reading of this book. They are the best generalizations and abstractions that psychologists have been able to develop, and they enable mental health workers to classify people and to make better use of limited medical resources. Nevertheless, they are labels and nothing more. In fact, they are very dangerous labels and should not be used casually. Calling someone neurotic, unbalanced, or mentally ill can be a severe injury, far more harmful to individual well-being than the symptoms upon which this diagnosis is based.

At the same time, there are real differences among the states of mental health of different individuals and within the same individual over a length of time. It is important to be able to differentiate between these different states, and the five stages which follow are useful ways of making this distinction clear. If used with caution, with the emphasis primarily on *understanding* rather than *grading* your mental health, they can be extremely helpful.

The problem is not to determine whether you are crazy or not, but to determine the degree to which the stresses and problems in your life reduce your adaptability. Everyone has problems. Everyone has defences. Everyone engages in behaviour that, from a clinical perspective, could be called abnormal. The diagnostic chart that follows enables you to judge to what extent your behaviour reflects a low level of adaptability. More importantly, it tells you in what areas your behaviour reflects these stresses and what kinds of activities and symptoms are worthy of legitimate concern and modification.

There is no hierarchy of human worth. If you are a stage three personality — Neurotic Coping Style — rather than stage one — Normal Adaptability — this does NOT mean that you are defective or inferior. Nor does it mean that you are superior or more sensitive. It is an indication that the stresses in your life are affecting your behaviour to a larger degree than that deemed normal or desirable for a happy, balanced life. This may be a reflection of social circumstances, a difficult family situation, a difficult childhood, a stressful job, financial problems, or a loss of religious or spiritual faith, or, more likely, a combination of these and other experiences in your life. All of these factors are capable of changing and no person is immune to stress or the removal of stress. Your mental health changes throughout time just as your physical health does. Despite Freudian claims to the contrary, there is little evidence suggesting the existence of defective personalities. Your state of mental health is a reflection of both personality traits and your immediate life-situation. Both factors are subject to change. With these warnings in mind, let us proceed to the practical application of the diagnostic chart which follows. In both the discussion and definition of the stages of mental health which follow, the terms normal, abnormal, neurotic, and psychotic will be used AS IF they were precise scientific labels. No values are implied in the use of these terms. This is a fiction but a useful one. Only in this way can an accurate picture be drawn of your mental health.

STAGE ONE: NORMAL ADAPTABILITY

There is nothing harder to define than normal behaviour. From a scientific point of view there is no such thing. The notion of normalcy is so embedded with cultural values that an objective cross-cultural definition (universal or comparative, which cuts across cultural or national differences) is impossible. What is normal for the Chinese strikes Britons as abnormal. The traditional male role as aggressors, organisers and decision makers is still held as the norm for some groups while to "liberated women" such a norm seems perverse and abnormal. At the same time, a woman brought up under the traditional patriarchal or matriarchal system is appalled at the indecent and abnormal behaviour of those who scorn her "backwardness". Views and values of what is normal can be compared, but there is no perspective from which we can rank or impose a true definition of normalcy. The best we can hope for is to define normalcy from a specific value perspective. For example, we could say that from the point of view of Americans in the U.S.A. who value the goals of democracy, self-determination, material possessions, and who believe as does Exxon that "the spirit of achievement is the spirit of America", normalcy is the ability to get along with others, to work, to preserve and further these American ideals while at the same time finding enjoyment and fulfilment in the exercise of those privileges and responsibilities which our American culture encourages. In Great Britain and other demo-cratic free countries similar values are held but this definition of normalcy would vary among different ethnic, geographical, and political groups.

Normalcy constitutes the "good life" for a particular group. Any definition can only be approximate and variable according to circumstances.

We have chosen for our definition of normalcy the idea of normal adaptability. This is as close to a universal definition as any that have been devised. It seems particularly appropriate for our society in the last quarter of the twentieth century in which our ability to adapt to the colossal and rapid changes brought about by technological and population expansion is sorely taxed. Never before in the history of the world have so many significant changes come about in the lifetimes of individual men. These changes are at all levels of society — the family (open marriages, divorces), politics (the cold war and the atom bomb), economics (work situations), communications (the world really is "shrinking" and approaching uniformity), and medical (people are living longer and with greater dependence on external devices than ever before).

The ability to adapt to these changes is becoming a necessity. Whether these changes are embraced as positive achievements (the dominant view) or viewed as works of the devil which are destroying the structure of our society (a significant minority position), they must be contended with. Men must adapt their lifestyles in such a manner as to make use of, or to protect themselves from, the effects of these changes.

On the individual level, this amounts to the ability to maintain a structure of meaning and coherence in one's daily life. Thus as an ideal, normalcy is a fluid condition in which the individual is able to maintain an operating balance and identify himself within society. A normal person is one who is able to make decisions and not merely react. He is resilient. He is able to accept the turns of fortune with, if not equanimity, at least a sense of balance. His life is an integrated whole and a failure in one area does not devalue his entire identity.

This requires that there be balance between work, love, and play — the Aristotelian ideal. An individual who is committed in equal measure to all three spheres of human life is less subject to disintegration than one who places all his emotional and physical energies in a single sphere. Life is full of changes. A man who places his entire self in the sphere of work, neglecting love (family) and play (sports, hobbies, socializing, friendships) decreases his overall adaptability. If he defines his existence in terms of achievement in his work, he will find that if for external reasons (poor health, old age, economic recession) or boredom (loss of interest, disillusionment with the larger purpose of his work, loss of faith in his employer) his work loses meaning, then so will his life. He will become demoralized, confused, and unable to function. The same is true in the spheres of love and play. A man or woman who defines existence in terms of a single love relationship will become demoralized if this relationship is destroyed. The relationship between unrequited love, broken love relationships, and mental illness is testimony to the danger of overinvesting all emotional energies in a single individual. In these cases, when there is a loss, there is nothing to take the place of the lost object or activity.

For this reason the notion of balance is at the core of the definition of normalcy. Only with balanced interests can an individual guard against the stress that loss or the threat of loss in a significant area produces. Losses must constantly be confronted in all human relationships and activities. This is the one constant in human experience; the inevitability of death. Only by participating fully in all three spheres of life — work, love, and play — is it possible to diminish the devastating effects of death in any single sphere. Balanced participation in the three spheres of life permits the experience of many losses which, in terms of the individual as a whole, are small "partial" deaths, *i.e.*, are less devastating than that of a single total loss so invested with meaning as to equal the death of the individual personality *in toto*.

In essence, normal adaptability implies the ability to function in everyday life: there may be inner conflicts but they do not impede your ability to act, to grow, and to change: your adaptation to your job, your family, and your social and cultural situation are relatively conflict-free: you do not question the basic facts of your existence but have a solid feeling of who you are, what you do, and why you do it: in the psychologist's terms you have a strong sense of identity: you may not like certain parts of your personality but you do not have difficulty defining yourself: you do not suffer from an identity crisis.

Checklist for Normal Adaptability

The following checklist covers the seven categories of behaviour characteristics outlined from page 15. Refer to these definitions before reading this section. Here are listed examples of behaviour for each characteristic that can be considered "normal". This list does not exhaust the possibilities of normal behaviour. It is best understood in comparison with the notes that follow on other stages of adaptability. Read through the checklist once briefly and then read it a second time, making light pencil marks next to those items which are applicable to your own behaviour. Do the same for the remaining four stages which follow.

1. TENSION

BEHAVIOUR

Tension has cause in the present or the past.
You can "do" something that helps to reduce tension when it arises.

Explanations and Examples

You do not experience tension or nervousness randomly. You do not find yourself tense or nervous for no apparent reason. You do become nervous under pressure. Whether this pressure is caused by a visit from your mother-in-law, the preparation for an important dinner party, or a public address that you must give is not significant. Each person faces acts or activities which create tension either in anticipation or performance. This is normal, particularly when there are concrete actions you can perform to reduce these tensions. These actions may consist of nothing more than discussing the anticipated visit from an in-law with a spouse and airing your worries, practising your speech in front of friends beforehand, or checking to be sure that you have all the ingredients at hand for a successful dinner party. It is not important what causes your tension, as long as you know what it is. Equally *what* you do to reduce tension (as long as it does not create significant additional problems, as may be the case with uncontrolled use of drugs or alcohol) is not so important as long as it works.

2. MOOD

BEHAVIOUR

Changes in mood have causes.

Presence of humour even when experiencing intense moods.

Moods can be intense but pass within a short time.

Explanation and Examples

Changes in mood have causes. A cause may be righteous indignation over a lie or unfair business practice perpetuated against you, producing a mood of intense anger. A romantic film in which the heroine dies may provoke a mood of sadness. What your mood is and what causes it is not as important as your ability to identify and gauge your reaction to specific events in everyday life.

Even when feeling angry or depressed you should still retain a sense of humour. A sense of humour is the ability to step back from yourself and your problems and enjoy either the humorous aspects of your own situation or that of others. The presence of a sense of humour includes the ability to enjoy the company of others and to be entertained. In short, it is the ability to laugh. When your anger or melancholy is so intense that you are unable to react to the whimsical and lighthearted, it is a sign of overvaluing a particular event or aspect of your life, of losing your mental balance.

The intensity of a mood, so long as the cause is appropriate, may be great. This is normal. What to look at is the duration of a mood. Do you find yourself staying angry for hours or days? When you're depressed, does it pass; do you respond to happier situations, or does the mood remain with you for days or even weeks?

3. THOUGHT

BEHAVIOUR

Able to secure and process information.
Thoughts of whatever kind do not upset for long.
Thoughts facilitate action.

Explanation and Examples

Normal thought behaviour is that in which you control your thoughts and in which thoughts implement action. In our culture "good thinking" is normal thinking. The ability to define a problem and think about the different kinds of information and different ways there are of organizing information toward a solution is characteristic of "good thinking".

Normal thinking is more than just problem-solving ability. Under thought behaviour are included fantasies, daydreams, and general contemplation. Sometimes fantasies and daydreams can be erotic (as with sexual fantasies) or exhilarating (sports fantasies) or frightening (highway commuter fantasies). Often they are disruptive and difficult to integrate with everyday life. The characteristic of normal thought is *not* the non-occurrence of such thoughts, but the ability to control them. Roughly it could be called the ability to "snap out of it" when your mind wanders off into your own private world.

Normal thought behaviour is that which is free of obsessive thoughts which interfere with the processing of information. It is the ability to relate to the external world in an active way. It is the ability to make decisions once you have processed information and to act upon information you have thought about. It is freedom from circular worrying and freedom from non-constructive thinking which does not contribute toward solving problems, providing satisfaction, or reducing anxiety.

4. ACTIVITY

BEHAVIOUR

Enthusiasm and interest in doing, participating — individually or in groups — in work or play, which brings a sense of competence.

Risk-taking and resilience — daring to be mediocre or fail, and to try again.

Activity may be uneven or continuous.

Explanation and Examples

Normal activity implies more than just going through the motions. Whether the activity is working, recreational, socializing, or love-making, it should bring a positive sense of self-fulfilment. Activity which brings a sense of competence also brings a sense of well-being. It helps to establish or re-establish your sense of identity and is a sign that you have a place in the world that is appreciated and valued by others.

A mentally adaptable person is not afraid to engage in new kinds of activities. He does not shun new experiences and new opportunities for growth. He is not afraid to take risks. He does not need constant success. He does not need to limit himself to those activities and those relationships in which he knows in advance that he will succeed or be warmly accepted. He is also not afraid of being just an average Joe. He is not afraid of being less than the best at everything. He is not a perfectionist and is willing to participate in areas of personal weakness as well as strength.

For example, is a successful businessman willing to be a mediocre tennis player or does he insist on playing only if he can achieve a high level of skill? Is an honours student in school willing to get on a dance floor and look a little foolish in front of her friends because she's not a very good dancer? Are you frightened of learning to play the guitar or of singing in a group because you're afraid you won't be any good? When you reject possible activities, even before trying them out because you're afraid of failing, your activity is not normal. (This, of course, varies for old people and for those with physical disabilities for whom risk-taking and engaging in new activities may be inappropriate. Even for these groups, however, within a range of safety, there should be a willingness to try new activities and make new friends.)

Even more important than risk-taking as a measure of good mental health is the notion of resilience. Resilience is your ability to recover from set-backs or failures. Most men who are successful in life are those who are able to recover after a disappointment and either try again or learn from their failures. Resilience, both mental and physical, decreases over time — you do not recover from injuries as rapidly. Failures become more difficult to accept in key areas of life, such as marriage and work. Nonetheless, as long as you survive you maintain a degree of resiliency, and in most cases, more than you give yourself credit for.

Normal behaviour is measured by your ability to engage in either uneven or continuous activities. Uneven activities are those which stop and start and require haphazard participation. Many games are of this nature. They require the ability to make sudden bursts of energy in specific areas. Continuous activities are those such as book-keeping or driving, which require constant attention over long periods of time. Each type of activity requires different qualities and the ability to engage in both types indicates a reserve of mental energies and general adaptability.

5.   ORGANIZATION/CONTROL

BEHAVIOUR

Can sit still and address self to task for increas-
   ingly long periods.
Can work in absence of inspiration or feedback.
Can plan and carry out solutions to multi-step
   problems.
Can learn from experience.
Possesses freedom to use behavioural repertoire
   flexibly.

Explanation and Examples

Normal organization/control behaviour has certain attributes in common with normal activity behaviour. How are your activities organized? Do you have patience and endurance for tedious tasks? Can you work alone without encouragement or rewards from others? Can you work well even when you're not in the mood to work? Can you carry out long-term projects which require careful preparation and planning? Do you learn from your failures and apply this knowledge to future projects? Are you able to call upon different kinds of behavioural skills in solving problems and to shift approaches smoothly and flexibly when necessary? If you answer "yes" to all of these questions you are clearly an adaptable and healthy individual.

An example of the freedom to use your behavioural repertoire flexibly is the ability to complete a project that requires different kinds of skills. A filmmaker who can sell his idea for making a film to investors, organize a film crew, and participate in the filming and meticulous editing process demonstrates a variety of behavioural skills, from interpersonal (selling the idea and organizing a crew) to concentration (editing) to intuitive and uneven (the actual filming). The work of a diplomat or a fund-raiser whose projects require the working out of long-term goals, dealing with a variety of different individuals and with unexpected events would also call upon a flexible repertoire of behavioural skills.

Again, as in all the characteristics discussed thus far, the appropriate behaviour for the mentally healthy is that which demonstrates the highest level of adaptability to the external world.

6. INTERPERSONAL

BEHAVIOUR

Rough coincidence with Sullivan's stages.
Be a friend as well as having friends.
Increasing capacity for intimacy.
Withdrawal or aggression have clear cause and eventually pass.

Explanation and Examples

Normal interpersonal behaviour is that in which you have a range of different kinds of relationships which

call forth different degrees of feeling and different
attitudes. You are able to be dependent on others and to
allow others to be dependent upon you.

Rough coincidence with Sullivan's stages refers to the
stages of personality development as described by
Harry Stack Sullivan (1892–1949). Sullivan developed
a theory of personality and interpersonal relations in
which each stage of development — infancy, childhood,
juvenile, preadolescence, early and late adolescence, and
mature adult — were associated with types of interpersonal skills. For instance, the juvenile era (5–9) is
associated with the abilities to compete, cooperate, and
compromise with others, but not with the ability to
establish intimacy, which is an interpersonal skill
achieved only in maturity. Sullivan argued that the
process of personality development was cumulative.
You could not demonstrate the higher interpersonal
skills until you had passed through the lower stages.
Sullivan cited many cases of "chronically juvenile"
people who were chronologically adults. By this he
meant that certain individuals never fully develop their
inter-personal skills. Although we do not accept
Sullivan's theory of stages as he presented it, it is useful
to think of approximate stages of growth and appropriate behaviour corresponding to different and
changing statuses. When an adult engages in childish
behaviour, is excessively competitive, or is unable to
establish intimacy, his behaviour does not coincide with
Sullivan's stages and is a sign of developmental arrest
and lack of normal interpersonal behaviour.

The capacity for intimacy is the ability to associate
closely with another. You are able to make yourself vulner-
able to another and share your most intimate thoughts and
feelings. You are also able to *accept* the vulnerability of
another without anxiety or destructive results. You give of
yourself from within; from you as you really are, and not
from the image that you try to project to the world at large.
The capacity for intimacy varies among different individuals, but all persons have needs for dealing with suf-

fering and personal despair which can only be satisfied by intimate relationships with others. In general, the greater the intimacy you achieve, the more productive your relationships will be with regard to your mental balance and behaviour in other areas.

The capacity for intimacy is not identical with the capacity to love, which may or may not be accompanied by intimacy.

It is normal to withdraw from another or even attack another when you are mistreated, insulted, humiliated, exploited, or otherwise have your trust abused. When you find yourself exploding against another, fighting, or uncomfortable it is important to know why this happens. When such antisocial behaviour occurs without provocation, or is resorted to before any attempt at communicating with another is made, this would be a case of abnormal interpersonal behaviour. Often a person will explode at another (especially a spouse or member of the immediate family) without knowing exactly why. To a certain extent this is normal, as many subtle messages are conveyed by persons who live together in close contact, which are often of an aggressive nature without being obvious. The repeated occurrence of such events, however, is not normal.

7. PHYSICAL

BEHAVIOUR

Stability of gastrointestinal system.
Stable skin and weight conditions.
Regular sleeping and breathing patterns.
Rapid recovery from illness/accident.
Sense of feeling well.

Explanation and Examples

Your physical health and your mental health are closely associated. Recent research is finding that many mental illnesses have physical correlates and that there is a close relationship between chemical and biological processes and mental behaviour. Apparently, your physical condition is both a cause and mirror of your mental condition.

Gastrointestinal problems are often signs of emotional stress. This is, of course, not always the case. Nonetheless, there is no better indicator of stable mental condition than a stable gastrointestinal system – regularity of bowel movements, comfortable digestion without excessive wind, and freedom from gastrointestinal problems such as heartburn, indigestion, nausea, diarrhoea, constipation, and associated stomach and intestinal illnesses.

One of the causes of acne and sudden weight losses and gains is emotional stress. The absence of major acne, and a stable weight condition are signs of mental health. The same is true of breathing and sleeping patterns. Although sleeping and breathing problems are not always the result of mental problems, the absence of insomnia, asthma, and rapid breathing are signs of positive mental health.

The rapid recovery from an accident or an illness is also a sign of mental health. Your mental condition often effects your rate of recovery from phsyical problems, and rapid and complete recovery is a positive sign. (Note that lengthy recovery is not necessarily a sign of mental illness, as physical causes may predominate over mental factors in many cases.) Likewise, a general sense of feeling well or of physical well-being is an important indicator of normal mental health.

STAGE TWO:
EMERGENCY REGULATORY BEHAVIOUR

In the above discussion of stage one behaviour, normal adaptability has often been used as if it referred to ideal adaptability, which is sought by all but obtained by few. To a certain extent this is true. No one is completely adaptable. There is no such thing as a perfectly normal person. We all have idiosyncracies and problems. It is possible to deviate from the behaviour suggested as normal and still be included in the general category of normal. This is the case of behaviour which falls into stage two: emergency regulatory behaviour. Again, no one is expected to exhibit precisely these behaviour symptoms.

Nonetheless, all of the following behaviour patterns are indicators of minor abnormality. They describe the behaviour of someone who is harassed or who is under extreme pressure. People are often under extreme pressure in our modern society, and some people hold jobs which are virtually constant emergency situations. For people in such situations the following behaviour patterns might indeed be normal and appropriate. The question in such a case would be to determine if your responsibilities are too great and if perhaps you would be happier in a less pressured job or life-situation. Behaviour problems in this stage often take care of themselves when external pressures are removed, and are not indicators of serious mental stress.

In general, the following conditions are "normal" adjustments to abnormal stress and strain. Such abnormal stresses might be school exams, deadline pressures at work, the break-up or loss of an important interpersonal relationship with girlfriend, parent, or child, and clear-cut external events such as economic loss, tragic world events, and deaths of persons upon whom you depend. Under such circumstances you can expect your usual resiliency and adaptability to be impaired. The purpose of the behaviour patterns which follow (a psychologist would call them defences) is to relieve tension, while permitting effective functioning. What is lost is general joy and adventure in living. You are forced to just get by and cannot really fulfil yourself. You cannot develop or enjoy your entire personality.

Nor can you appreciate and constructively enjoy opportunities which you might have, were you behaving in accordance with stage one patterns.

Checklist for Emergency Regulatory Behaviour

1. TENSION

BEHAVIOUR

Clear-cut signs of tension (agitation, sweating, rapid breathing).

Tension has a cause (exams, disrupted personal relations, pending operation).

Tension may or may not inhibit work.

Explanation and Examples

In stage two it is not as easy to reduce tension as in stage one. Signs of tension are much clearer and occur more frequently. Your nervousness is, however, still in response to immediate and understandable causes. You do not start sweating spontaneously or become agitated for no apparant reason. You show signs of stress, but only in response to real stresses in your environment — loss of a job, the need for surgery, a divorce, etc. Despite your tension, you will probably still be able to carry out your normal responsibilities. At times you may find normal work more burdensome and use your tension "symptoms" to avoid normal activities. Your precise reactions will vary according to other factors, such as mood and physical well-being, but you are not at the point at which your tension prohibits you from engaging in work and carrying out normal responsibilities.

2.   MOOD

BEHAVIOUR

Sense of being easily upset, moody, intolerant.
Explosive humour as tension release.

Explanation and Examples

In stage two, your moods change frequently and are more intense. You are less stable and small problems and disappointments can make you suddenly depressed. You don't have your normal bounce and enthusiasm. When contradicted you become upset. You do not appreciate surprises or the unexpected as much as you normally would, and you can become intolerant of anyone who does not pay extra attention to your particular mood (happy or sad).

A common symptom in stage two is to become uncustomarily demonstrative of your emotions; to explode with laughter as a means of releasing your built-up tension, or to suddenly start crying or to explode with angry shouting. You will still be responding to actual situations – a funny joke, a tragic book or film, poor or inefficient service, inadequate attention. The difference will be in the intensity of your response and the need to release tension in socially acceptable ways; ways upon which you did not previously rely.

3.   THOUGHT

BEHAVIOUR

Thoughts intensely, narrowly, and continuously focused on task or problem.
Tension release through thoughts – passive, aggressive, sexual.
Selective inattention.

Explanation and Examples

In stage two you must struggle with your thoughts in order to act effectively. You do not experience free-flowing, constructive thinking. Problem-solving is not effortless but demands concentrated thinking which is intense and immediate. You cannot allow thoughts to wander, for fear of not being able to return to the problem at hand. You can only think about one problem or a single stage of a problem at a time. Your thoughts are reactions to situations and not creations.

The reason you must focus on narrow issues is that you are trying to release tension through thoughts. You imagine acts of aggression against your enemies or have sexual fantasies or daydreams in which all your problems are solved without any effort on your part. Such fantasies are normal, but in stage two they occur more frequently and serve to distract you from solving your problems in real life. Rather than facilitating action as in stage one, your thoughts prevent and inhibit effective action. You still function and get the job done, but it's more of a struggle.

In stage two you might also find yourself ignoring situations or people that upset you. You will turn yourself off rather than risk potential frustration at hearing things or seeing things you'd rather not think about. Your inattention is selective, however. You do not ignore really important information and are still able to make important decisions and to process difficult information.

4. ACTIVITY

BEHAVIOUR

According to temperament, lots of activity or little.
Anxiety about new risks or overload.
Talismanic words, behaviour.

Explanation and Examples

In stage two your activity level is no longer smooth and stable. You may find yourself cutting down on your activities or scurrying about hurriedly, taking on far more than is possible for the time at your disposal. According to temperament, you are less likely to involve yourself with new activities and are cautious about overextending yourself. You are very much aware of what activities you engage in and are more anxious about how well you will do than in stage one.

Because you have less confidence in your abilities and are more concerned with how your activities demonstrate to others your general state of being and your worth, in stage two you are likely to seek tricks and gimmicks which will assure success. To a certain extent this use of ritualistic behaviour is normal. By always repeating certain speeches or ritual acts you assure yourself a sense of continuity. Such talismanic behaviour is common among athletes who may always play the same song before a contest or wear the same pair of socks while on a hitting streak.

In stage two you are far more dependent on following a set routine in order to assure success. You are not able to shift as easily from one type of activity to another. You still enjoy your activities but your motivation is as much the anxiety you feel if you don't keep busy, as the positive pleasure of action itself.

5.   ORGANIZATION/CONTROL

BEHAVIOUR

Anxiety stimulates action.
May lie or cheat under pressure.

Explanation and Examples

In stage two your anxiety directs your action. Your organization is less creative and you will use any means possible to assure a positive outcome. You need to play with a loaded pack, to be sure that nothing unexpected will occur to complicate your plans. You may still be able to engage in complicated problem-solving and long-term planning, but your tolerance of ambiguity or uncertainty is low.

An example of emergency regulatory behaviour is that carried out by Nixon's campaigners in 1972, which resulted in the Watergate scandal. Nixon and some of his associates felt themselves under such extreme pressure to win the election that they were willing to rationalize unethical procedures as justified in the light of the importance (they maintained and tried to make themselves believe) to national security of a Nixon victory.

Had a true emergency existed, their behaviour might have been justifiable as normal emergency behaviour. Given the actual realities, it was a sign of a more general breakdown.

In stage two the results of your organization and control may be identical to those achieved under normal mental health. The difference is the quality of your planning. You are less likely to come up with elegant or creative solutions and more likely to rely on drudgery and anxiety-directed doggedness to get the job done. Your work is just as effective, but you enjoy it less.

6.   INTERPERSONAL

BEHAVIOUR

May use upset feelings manipulatively to seek attention.
Anxiety about pleasing others.
Unwillingness or inability to "play".
Over-emotional in interpersonal relationships.
Irritable.

Explanation and Examples

When under emergency stress, interpersonal behaviour is that which deteriorates most. You begin to see yourself as a special person entitled to special consideration. When you're upset you may use your depression or anger as a means of forcing friends or family to take notice of your problems and to give you special attention and understanding. In stage two you are often irritable, ready to fly off the handle at the least provocation.

You are less willing to tolerate horseplay or any activity which pokes fun at you or the things you value. Your ability to compromise or cooperate with others may be reduced and it is harder to achieve intimacy than in stage one. You take yourself and others much more seriously than necessary and do not have your normal good humour and pleasant disposition.

You are anxious to please others and gain their approval. You overreact to criticism and negative feedback. You exaggerate mild disapproval and create friction between yourself and others without intending to. You also become over-emotional, showing disproportionate concern or affection for people you aren't really close to. You react less to people as they really are and more as you pretend they are in some ideal world which exists in your mind more than in the everyday world. As a result, you are less able to appreciate the real strengths and weaknesses of your friends and have more difficulty in establishing a wide range of appropriate relationships of different intensities.

In stage two, however, you still have many friends and are able to appreciate their individual qualities, especially in moments of calm or when the stresses of your emergency lifestyle or job have passed. You are still pretty much in control of your interpersonal relationships.

7. PHYSICAL

BEHAVIOUR

Fluctuations in eating and sleeping patterns and in
   weight.
Minor gastrointestinal problems, skin blemishes.
Physical sense of tension, tiredness, of using
   physical reserves.
Conscious use of drugs to cope.

Explanation and Examples

In stage two you may find yourself overeating,
having difficulty getting to sleep, or suffering from
stomach problems such as wind and indigestion. If you
are an adolescent or young adult you may be plagued
by acne and skin blemises. You may even have an
outbreak of hives or a skin rash.

Physically you don't feel 100 per cent. You have a
feeling of being pushed to the limits of your endurance,
of not having your normal "get up and go." You
become tired easily and your muscles are often stiff.
You are more accident-prone than normal and when ill
recover more slowly.

To deal with these problems, you may find yourself
taking non-prescription sleeping pills, mild tranquillizers, or stimulants (both legal drugs and illegal drugs
ranging from aspirin to pot or speed). You may also find
yourself drinking more alcohol than usual. Nonetheless,
in stage two you are conscious of what drugs or
stimulants you take and are aware of their effects upon
you and why you are taking them. They do serve to
reduce tension and you are able to dispense with them
when not under pressure. Above all you are not dependent upon drugs to get through a normal day and do not
take drugs automatically when anything goes wrong.
Prescription medicines taken outside medical advice
and illegal drugs are danger signals of incipient mental

problems. It is hoped this book will keep you clear of them.

STAGE THREE: NEUROTIC COPING STYLES

Stage three behaviour is emergency behaviour in absence of emergencies. You are constantly under pressure regardless of external realities. You have major problems in at least one sphere of behaviour (work, play, or love) and you find it necessary to reorganize your behaviour repertoire in order to reduce tension. Your freedom of action is compromised and you find yourself forced to give up much enjoyment in life because you are afraid of putting yourself in a situation you can't handle. Nonetheless, you are still able to use your personal and mental resources – skills, interests, friends – to cope with your problems. In fact, in stage three you are able to accomplish most tasks and at least go through the motions of normal social and economic life; fulfilling duties and obligations to friends, family, and co-workers. The major difference is that you are going through the motions rather than positively reacting to yourself, others, and your life. You do not enjoy challenges and even though you find yourself able to satisfactorily get through even difficult situations, you prefer to restrict your activities and reduce, as far as possible, any demands that might be made upon you.

Checklist for Neurotic Coping Styles

1. TENSION

BEHAVIOUR

Signs of tension with no apparent cause.
Tension inhibits work.

Explanation and Examples

In stage three, you experience tension and attacks of anxiety without apparent cause. Common signs are sweating, rapid breathing, and feeling fidgety. You have these attacks not only in response to difficult situations, as in stage two, but also as common occurrences in day-to-day living. You may find yourself suffering from headaches or muscular soreness which makes work painful if not impossible. You can still do enough to get by, but you are really only coping and not determining your own existence.

In stage three you are still able to reduce tension by avoiding unpleasant situations and by relying on positive action. Your nervousness comes and goes and does respond, at least partially, to events in your environment. You are not incapable of experiencing moments of calm or of feeling perfectly relaxed. Such comfortable states are, however, more noticeable by their absence than by their occurrence.

2. MOOD

BEHAVIOUR

Moods lasting beyond time when recovery should occur (as in depression).

Intermittent hysterical behaviour; denial of problems; hyperemotional expressions without, or out of keeping with, apparent cause; without awareness.

Hostile wit.

Mild chronic fears and phobias.

Counterphobic behaviour with some risk.

Blocked specific emotions (love, hate), resulting in bland responses when more is called for.

Explanation and Examples

In stage three, moods are an important indicator of lessened adaptability. Moods last much longer than you would normally expect. Something may happen to depress or upset you, but instead of coming out of a depressed mood in a few hours or days, you may be depressed for weeks. This is the case even though pleasant events occur subsequently. For example, you may be depressed over an unsuccessful romantic relationship. This would be normal. If at the same time you received news of an important promotion, were given a surprise party by some close friends, and won a football betting pool and still remained depressed, this would be an indication of abnormal mood behaviour and a significant danger signal.

Another possible symptom would be intermittent hysterical behaviour, such as irrational behaviour, temper tantrums, crying fits, or strong denials of your problems and weaknesses. Hysterical behaviour is that which, as seen by outsiders, is clearly an attempt to release tension by denying reality. You are not really aware of what you are saying; you jump from feeling totally depressed to feeling suddenly elated for no apparent reason. You read into acts of others motives which are not there. If someone compliments you, you think that he (or she) is in love with you or is going to offer you a promotion. If someone is abrupt with you, you think that they hate you. On reflection, you might realize afterwards that this is not the case, but your immediate reaction is to treat others as if this were obviously the intent behind their actions. Of course it isn't (generally), and from their perspective your behaviour is hysterical.

If incidents like this occur occasionally, with friends telling you that something is wrong, you don't have to worry if you are able to understand what is going on and to control your behaviour. More likely, however, in stage three you will react by protesting that nothing's the matter and that you're perfectly fine. This would be a case of "I think he doth protest too much" and further evidence of more serious mental problems.

Another common way of dealing with stage three-type mental stress is with hostile wit. You use your wit to make nasty or biting comments about others which may be humourous but are clearly aggressive and hostile. This is an effective way of releasing inner rage without totally transgressing social norms. You are able to keep yourself from physically attacking others, but the hostility of your humour belies your mood and your thoughts. You don't go around hitting or killing people, but you would like to.

An alternate way of dealing with rage or anxiety in stage three is by directing your anger against yourself. This results in mild chronic fears and phobias. A mild chronic fear might be an inability to criticize your boss or a fear of aeroplanes that prevents you from flying. A mild phobia might be a fear of snakes or a fear of rats, even in captivity. As long as such phobias are mild and do not affect your daily life or come up often, you are still coping with life, although perhaps a bit neurotically.

As a reaction against your fears and phobias you might demonstrate the exact opposite behaviour. This would be the same pattern as denying fears and problems — "the self doth protest too much" syndrome. For example, the man who is afraid of criticizing his boss even when it is warranted, suddenly begins to insult him for no apparent reason. The person who is afraid of flying decides to take up parachute-jumping; the woman who is afraid of snakes enters a snake farm, and so on. These would be cases of counterphobic behaviour, and if engaged in without proper precautions and preparations, could endanger the health or well-being of the individual.

Finally, people in stage three often find their strongest emotions blocked. They are so intent on controlling their moods and their feelings that they are unable to let themselves go and express their true feelings toward someone they love or hate. It is unusual for this symptom to be combined with the other symptoms of over-emotional expressions and hostile wit, but sometimes they do occur simultaneously. Some psychologists hypothesize that so much emotional energy is being wasted in overreacting to people you don't really care about and in exaggerating your reactions to other people who are actually quite insignificant to you, that emotionally you have nothing left for those you really care about. A common example is the employer who goes out of his way to help and be considerate of casual acquaintances but is unable to express his love to his wife or to share in her emotions. He has no trouble expressing appropriate feelings with people who are not very close to him emotionally, but has trouble establishing or maintaining intimacy with those who are. Though he may be overjoyed at an accomplishment of his spouse, he is unable to offer more than a "That's nice, dear." Again, as has been emphasized above, in stage three there is little real enjoyment in one's accomplishments or in sharing with others. You are functioning, coping, and going through the motions but not living with your full self.

3. THOUGHT

BEHAVIOUR

Tendency to analyse rather than experience feeling.

Questions ability to feel important emotions.

Worrying circularly about things that could happen; brings momentary respite but doesn't lead to constructive action.

Explanation and Examples

A good example of stage three thought (and stage three behaviour, in general) is that of Mary Hartman in the television series "Mary Hartman, Mary Hartman". Mary is constantly hassled. She analyses her relationships with others — I did this, therefore Tom hates me, Tom doesn't communicate with me therefore he doesn't love me — but she is seldom able to experience feelings of anger, warmth, or love. She knows analytically that she loves her sister and her husband but she isn't in touch with these feelings. When her real feelings come up she diverts conversations to other subjects like waxing the floor and drinking coffee.

Other examples of stage three thought are provided by people who question their ability to love or their ability to feel affection, hate, or any strong emotion for another. They are so wrapped up in themselves and their problems that they question their ability to interact fully with another.

A common symptom of neurotic coping is circular worrying. This kind of worrying occurs quite frequently in anxiety-ridden individuals. They hypothesize possible malfunctions and problems, many of which are unlikely to occur. When they go on a trip they make elaborate reservations, planning their entire trip to the smallest detail. Yet they still worry that a relative will get sick, that reservations will be broken, that they will misplace their travel documents, etc. Most important, they don't do anything to prevent these possible occurrences (often because they're the kind of thing you can't prevent) and their worrying does not lead to positive action (for example, buying a travel pouch to keep all important documents in one place instead of just worrying about how you can be extra careful not to lose them). Circular worrying is more than ordinary concern about the outcome of a possible event; it is concern which is unproductive in dealing with the external factors which actually influence events. It is more akin to fantasizing and daydreams than rational planning. Again, occasional instances of such worrying are normal. In stage three, however, such worrying is frequent.

4. ACTIVITY

BEHAVIOUR

Hyperactivity with no point, often accompanied
by sense of exhaustion.
Activity still reduces tension.
Requires inspiration or feedback to work well.
Marked reduction in risk-taking.

Explanation and Examples

In stage three, activity is not fluid. There are sudden
spurts of energy and periods of total inertia. A common
symptom is hyperactivity which leads nowhere. You
run around doing a hundred different things practically
simultaneously but doing nothing well or completely.
You do not work calmly and steadily. You may have
difficulty getting anything done or getting up enough
enthusiasm to start new projects. Then suddenly you
want to make up for your last three weeks of lethargy
and start to compress into a few days, weeks of activity
that you have put off. Such patterns of activity are
serious danger signals that you are undergoing mental
stress.

In stage three you are still in relative control of your
actions. You can finish some tasks and you can work
well under ideal conditions. You get some satisfaction
from your work, at least a minor sense of competence or
self-justification. Your work makes life easier to take.
But without encouragement or a positive working
environment you have difficulty keeping yourself
involved with your work. You need constant approval
and appreciation from your employer and co-workers.
You need to be reminded that your work is important or
necessary and that your efforts are appreciated. You
cannot work well on ambiguous projects or on tasks in
which you define the goals and evaluation criteria
yourself. You need support from others and become less

creative and less independent in all your endeavours.

This state carries over into your non-professional activities as well. You find it difficult to make decisions – even to decide what to order for dinner or where to sit in a theatre or what film to see. To some extent, occasional bouts of indecision and insecurity over your decision-making ability is normal. In stage three, such occurrences are frequent. In stage three, you rarely take a risk or try something new. You are unsure of your ability to adapt to new people or new challenges and prefer to stick with the tried and true; not only in fundamental areas of your life, in which a wrong decision could be costly, but even in non-threatening situations in which it is either not significant or not possible to make a wrong choice – where to have dinner, what shade of lipstick to wear, or where to spend your vacation.

5.   ORGANIZATION/CONTROL

BEHAVIOUR

Increased rigidity: desires clear-cut demands and perfectly tailored work/school environment to function.

Chronic condition of being over-extended, resulting in forgetfulness, shortcuts, occasionally shoddy work which can be upsetting to self or others.

Unpredictable events disrupt performance badly.

Occasional impulsive behaviour.

Rituals (sharpening pencils) interfere with work.

Limited capacity for self-generated insight and change.

Explanation and Examples

Stage three organization and control behaviour is similar to that of number 4, neurotic coping ACTIVITY behaviour. You have little flexibility or creativity in your organizational efforts. Everything must be "just so" in order to function. You cannot tolerate ambiguity or open-ended projects. Goals must be clearly defined; procedures clearly laid out. There is no room for innovation or unexpected modifications of demands. You want and need direct commands and clear objectives. It is not sufficient to know general goals; you need specifics in work situations and social situations as well. Before meeting someone you must know exactly what they're like and how to treat them.

Because this need for rigidity in organizing your life is almost impossible to achieve, given the fluidness and unpredictability of most of life, you often find yourself over-extended, doing work which is not up to your own standards, or which is clearly not up to your sense of your potential. Because rigid organization requires planning for events which infrequently occur, much effort is wasted and you take longer to get your work done. You often demonstrate perfectionist behaviour, spending too much time with details which aren't really very important. As a result, you end up forgetting more significant procedures or taking shortcuts which reduce the quality of your work. This combination of over-valuing certain aspects of a project and under-valuing others is a clear sign of the instability and imbalance generated by mental stresses in stage three.

Your adaptability is reduced. Unexpected delays or last minute changes in plans are intolerable; they completely destroy your ability to work or enjoy yourself. If you plan a camping trip and, because of a flat tyre, arrive too late to find a camping site, you become completely demoralized and unable to adjust smoothly. Eventually you are able to cope with this unforeseen difficulty (by going somewhere else, finding a motel, camping along the road, or even sleeping in the car) but only after experiencing extreme anxiety, frustration, or anger. In stage three you are able to cope and you often hit on very good plans and solutions to difficult problems but you are only coping and it is a painful process. This is in contrast to someone in stage one who might have less imagination about what to do in such a predicament but is calmer, steadier, and more confident that he'll be able to arrange some adequate alternative. In stage three you minimize your efforts and organizational abilities while in stage one you maximize your mental and real resources.

Occasional compulsive behaviour includes reading every book on a course reading list, even though you know that it's not required or expected by your professor. Suddenly deciding to take off from work to go to the beach, buying clothes you don't really need, or suddenly deciding to dye your hair while at the beautician are examples of impulsive behaviour. Such impulsive acts are not necessarily signs of stage three, but when they are disruptive or out of character, they are probable danger signals.

In stage three, ritualistic behaviour becomes much more common. You find that little rituals provide tension release. The result of these momentary defences is, however, often disruptive or counterproductive. You spend more time clearing up your desk in preparation for work you have to do than in the actual work. You develop a series of rigid behaviour patterns in which you have to go through a number of often unnecessary steps to get something done. Your behaviour becomes mechanized. You have a set response which does not vary, even though the input does. You treat all problems as if they were identical. You are unable to adapt to the particularities and subtle differences between problems.

You have difficulty learning from experience. Because you try to force everything and everyone into set patterns, you are unable to change and to grow. Your rigid responses are incapable of perceiving individual differences. You react to problems rather than acting on them. You are afraid to experiment with new strategies or to stray from tried solutions. You are cautious about changing behaviour patterns and seek situations with which you are comfortable and which pose few threats. You do not experiment or modify your plans or your behaviour. You do not generate changes but passively react to your environment. You are more often acted upon rather than being the actor. You have difficulty in directing and defining yourself and your life. You get by, sometimes very satisfactorily, but your successes and happiness depend more on the actions of others than on any self-realizing behaviour. You feel that your life is not as full as it might be and that you are not reaching your potential.

6.   INTERPERSONAL

BEHAVIOUR

Moving toward, against, or away from others in overdriven or inappropriate manner.

Demands others do what he or she wants.

Mild separation anxiety (school phobia); can be scapegoated or bullyish.

Can throw self prematurely into one-to-one relationship.

Changing, deteriorating friendships often featured by grudges.

May have a sense of being admired, respected, but (1) may feel nothing without continual external support, or (2) actively doubt worthiness.

Mild anti-social behaviour or alienation.

Explanation and Examples

In stage three you overreact to others. You have a need to create strong bonds with others, which is not being fulfilled. As a result you seize inappropriate moments – such as trying to make a date with a girl who is having dinner with another boyfriend – in which to try to establish contact. You expect more from casual acquaintances than most other people and try to force yourself upon others. When rejected or even when your attentions are merely returned without the intensity behind your own, you became disappointed and often angry. You then go to the opposite extreme and, for some minor argument, reject entirely someone who the previous day you had hoped would become an intimate friend.

In stage three you have a compulsion to get your own way always. Everybody has to play by your rules and you regard yourself as the centre of the universe. You have difficulty giving to others and seek constant signs of reassurance or of affection from those you love or respect. You become very anxious when you have to leave a set of friends or enter a new group of friends. You react as does a child when he first goes to school and gets very frightened, sometimes including physical symptoms such as vomiting at the prospect of having to leave the security of the family home. In a less dramatic way you too become frightened at the prospect of separating yourself from those you have depended upon in the past. Incidents may come up with regard to changing jobs, receiving a promotion, having neighbours and family move away, etc.

To deal with the anxiety you feel in entering new groups you seek extreme interpersonal stances of withdrawal or aggression. If you choose withdrawal you become passive, allowing others to order you around, make fun of you, or blame you every time anything goes wrong. By seeking such low-status roles in groups you avoid the anxiety of asserting yourself on a give-and-take basis. You don't have to fear rejection because you know you belong and the price of self-humiliation does not strike you as excessive, given your fears and inability to establish satisfying relationships in other ways. The other alternative would be to bully others into accepting you. They may accept you out of fear, but again you illustrate a stage three failing of being unable to interact with others on an equal footing.

In stage three your social life is unbalanced. You

establish sudden intimacies which deteriorate and fall apart. You throw yourself into romantic relationships which you know are unlikely to survive. You consciously ignore factors about another which you know will create problems later on (i.e. inappropriate educational level, politically on the left while you are right-centre, widely different interests, etc.).

The friendships you do have experience constant crises. Disputes erupt frequently, many of them resulting in grudges of both long and short duration. You find it difficult to overlook or forgive faults in others. You seek perfection, both in yourself and in others. You have difficulty accepting actions which are generated by the frailty or weaknesses of others and try to ignore such weaknesses in yourself.

Because you have a distorted and unrealistic attitude toward the way in which people interact, substituting the ideal for the actual, you feel particularly rotten when you see that you don't measure up to the standards that you hold for others. The fact that these standards are unrealistic escapes you and you are left with a sense of worthlessness. Instead of merely realizing that you, like everyone else, are not perfect either in thought or in deed, you overreact and feel that you are a totally worthless or inadequate person. This sense of worthlessness penetrates even your strongest relationships with self-doubts which can only be relieved by continual assurances of your strength, good humour, or general likeability by friends, colleagues, and lovers. Often you really do possess the superior qualities you feel you show but your inability to accept your weaknesses prevents you from feeling confident and secure. Your constant need to be petted and praised often creates tensions among those who care most about you.

Mild anti-social behaviour includes selfishness, callousness to others, and overall irresponsibility. Such anti-social behaviour is generally impulsive, a case of seeking personal pleasure without regard to the consequences of one's actions. More than a lack of consideration or bad manners, anti-social behaviour has an undercurrent of hostility. Alienation is a general feeling of not belonging or not sharing the values of the society in which you live. You do not feel comfortable accepting that which those around you take for granted. There are many legitimate reasons, both existential and political, for feeling alienated from modern society, but in stage three, alienation occurs not so much because you are consciously trying to create a different value system or relationship to the world but because you are unable to fit into society as it exists. You feel blind rage against the external world and can't identify the legitimate causes of your suffering. By blaming society for your problems you are able to preserve the illusion that you have few internal mental problems and that unknown others are responsible for your shortcomings.

7. PHYSICAL

BEHAVIOUR

Obesity, lack of appetite, sleep disturbances.
More serious, as well as minor, gastrointestinal problems.
Intermittent skin problems, headaches.
Physical tics, stuttering.
Resorting to drugs/medical help to "feel better".
Episodic drug abuse, socially reinforced.

Explanation and Examples

A common symptom of neurotic coping behaviour is chronic overeating, resulting in obesity. You eat not because you are hungry but in order to release tensions. You have little self-control about what you eat and find it impossible to refuse any food you really enjoy regardless of not feeling hungry. You become a compulsive eater, not cutting down even though you know that being overweight endangers your physical health and diminishes your ability to participate in a wide range of physical activities. You also become less attractive.

The opposite symptom, lack of appetite, is an alternative manifestation of the same stresses that create overeaters. Not eating is a way of withdrawing and punishing yourself, just as overeating is an aggressive action against your person. Both patterns of behaviour attack your body and are important signs of inner stress. Of course, there may be purely physical reasons in some cases for overeating or lack of appetite, but in most cases they are important indicators of mental problems.

Not being able to sleep at night and waking up in the middle of the night or very early in the morning are also signs of inner conflicts. Chronic oversleeping is another possible indicator, usually associated with mild cases of depression.

Middle level gastrointestinal problems include minor problems such as stomach upset, flatulence, and diarrhoea which become chronic. If such ailments become permanent aspects of your digestive behaviour, more serious physical problems may result.

In stage three headaches become much more common as do hives and other types of skin rashes. Phsyical tics, such as always winking your eye or moving your left wrist in a particular way before speaking may also occur. Such physical tics are unconscious and uncontrollable. You are not aware that you have these automatic responses until someone points them out to you. Sometimes they disappear naturally but they are generally related to mental stress. Stuttering in most cases is also related to nervousness and anxiety. Even when there are physical causes of the problem, the mental dimension should also be considered and treated.

A sign that your physical behaviour is beginning to break down is the need to take medication just to feel better or feel right. You do not take drugs or aspirin for specific physical ailments but just to relieve general tension. You become dependent on sleeping pills and other tranquillizers or stimulants, resorting to them whenever you're feeling a little off.

Episodic or frequent use of illegal drugs such as marijuana is another indicator. To use such drugs occasionally, especially given the social pressures to indulge existing in many subgroups, is not necessarily indicative of mental conflicts. But when usage becomes daily or as often as three or four times a week, there are probably mental stresses involved in your usage as well. The same would be true in the case of alcohol. In both cases, you know you have problems when you can no longer control your intake of these substances. It is this dependence and overindulgence that indicates under-lying mental problems, not the substances *per se*. At the same time you should be aware that different people react differently to drugs and that there are cases in which marijuana and other stimulants have aggravated mental problems.

STAGE FOUR: NEUROTIC CHARACTERS

Stage four behaviour is an intensification of stage three behaviour symptoms. Your neurotic coping devices have become permanent parts of your personality. Your maladaptive behaviour is consistent and predictable. Unlike stage three behaviour, which can respond to positive opportunities in your environment and diminish or grow, stage four behaviour continues in spite of environmental opportunities to behave differently. Even when others treat you in an ideal fashion you exhibit disruptive or destructive behaviour. You do not take advantage of opportunities to grow.

Also in stage four you begin to make an organizational adjustment to problem behaviour. You can't really cope. Certain motions you are able to go through in stage three stop altogether. Your problems are such that you must abandon responsibilities, take time off from work, or restructure your daily routine in order to get through the day.

Your maladaptive behaviour is further removed from the external causes of stress. You have internalized stressful situations to the point that they occur spontaneously and are almost unrelated to what actually goes on in your interactions with persons and things. You become angry for apparently no reason. You perceive threats where none exist. You react to what you think others want to do or say and not to what they actually do or say.

Your maladaptive behaviour is tenaciously and vigorously maintained even in the face of serious resistance by others. You do not adapt to procedures or institutions about you but expect and often cause fellow workers, school friends, or others with whom you come into contact to alter their procedures to accommodate your special needs.

You can reduce anxiety only by closing your cognitive field to restrict and avoid new stimuli. You try to take in as few new perceptions as possible about your problems. You are unable to learn anything about your original problem because you have lost the ability to look at yourself calmly and objectively. You exaggerate and underestimate both your weaknesses and strengths. The only acceptable solution is to choose a particular interpretation of yourself which allows you to survive without total chaos. You want to avoid scrutinizing your behaviour and your problems because you are afraid of what you'll find; you are afraid of breaking down entirely and being completely unable to cope.

In stage four at least two of the three spheres of life (work, love, and play) are seriously impaired. You may be experiencing serious problems at work or interpersonal problems at home or an inability to do anything but work, sacrificing completely the spheres of love and play. You may be unable to organize your behaviour or control your thoughts. Nonetheless, often a single sphere, a particularly gratifying relationship, a successful career, an enthusiastic sport or hobby enables you to cope and function moderately well.

Perhaps the greatest difference between stage three and stage four behaviour is that in stage four your resources are consumed or their use blocked. You have reached the end of the line. You can no longer rely on your abilities, friends, interests, and positive strengths to get you through crises. In stage three you are still able to help yourself. This becomes increasingly difficult in stage four. In stage three you can still get by, with a little help from your friends. In stage four you may need more formal intervention or the aid of a professional.

Checklist for Neurotic Characters

1. TENSION

BEHAVIOUR

May feel less chronic tension than before due to use of strong defences.

Periods of nearly unbearable anxiety with no obvious cause.

Explanation and Examples

Instead of feeling tension about trying to establish a romantic relationship you give up completely and avoid meeting or trying to establish an intimate relationship. You feel tension in going to work so you stop going. You have difficulty accepting a dependent role so you become aggressive and unapproachable. You feel weak and helpless so you exaggerate your abilities in a particular area and delude yourself with feelings of grandiosity and invincibility. All such behaviour patterns reduce your experience of tension but at the cost of distorting or limiting your view of yourself and life.

When you give up these defences or do not concentrate on fighting off your anxieties you may
experience almost unbearable anxiety. Such attacks
may have both physical and mental manifestations,
from being unable to move, feeling extreme stiffness in
your entire body, nausea and pains in the pit of your
stomach, to suicidal tendencies, experiencing macabre
thoughts, and feeling that you are going to explode.
Whatever manifesations of anxiety you exhibited in the
lower stages become more severe and they occur in
absence of any specific cause. You feel as if you're
falling apart at the seams or that everything is on the
verge of going out of control. You're in a panic and
unable to reduce tension by merely relaxing or seeking
normal comforts.

2. MOOD

BEHAVIOUR

Background moods affect work, love, play.

Chronic depressed, unhappy states (suicide
    attempts), nihilism; no amount of support or
    reassurance helps.

May get "high" on ideas or plans; but problems in
    finishing or following through.

Phobias affect enjoyment and productivity.

Self-destructive counterphobic acting out.

Predictable hysterical behaviour (destructibility,
    outbursts, impressionability).

Explanation and Examples

You are strongly influenced by the moods of those
about you. You react to changes in weather much more
intensely, feeling joyful when it's sunny and morose
when it's grey. If there is tension or irritability at the
office (among others, not involving you) you find yourself unable to work effectively. Sentimental songs make

you sad, angry songs make you angry, and these emotions carry over to your activities. You are more susceptible to moodiness than in previous stages.

You may be chronically depressed or experience a general feeling of doom and despair. Or you can become nihilistic, wanting to destroy everything and everybody, delighting in the contemplation that ultimately everything will be destroyed and no human accomplishment remain. Your general pessimism, uncertainty, apathy, or sadness is not diminished even when those you care about comfort you and reassure you of your worth. You feel that you and all your efforts are meaningless failures, and this feeling does not disappear even when contradicted by those in a position to judge. In stage three you may have exhbited similar feelings of despair but your depression was affected and mitigated by your friends. In stage four nothing seems to help. Your conflicts are too complicated and too weighty. You feel that no one can understand you and that praise or comfort cannot alleviate your problems.

When you do come out of your depression you may get "high" on ideas or plans. You become elated and super-enthusiastic, almost as if on a drug trip. Your thinking goes very fast and you have insights into yourself and others that you never had before. You feel that you have finally found a solution to what had seemed insurmountable problems. Or you may have an idea for a project at work or a social event for which you begin to make elaborate plans. You are bubbling over with enthusiasm and energy. You talk about your plans with others and they seem genuinely impressed and supportive of your good ideas. But the crunch comes in following through or finishing these projects. The tremendous enthusiasm which you originally had suddenly disappears. Where at the start you overstated the importance of your insights or projects, you now devalue them entirely. Somehow you no longer understand how you could have got so excited. Your ideas no longer seem so brilliant and you lose faith in your abilities. You go back into a low until another high comes along, repeating the pattern.

Phobias and fears prevent you from enjoying yourself or working effectively. Past failures or situations seem destined to repeat themselves. Even when things are going well, you are frightened that a disaster will strike or that some basic personality flaw will be revealed and catch you up in a humiliating or destructive failure. To counteract these fears, you purposely put yourself in difficult situations in which you will be called upon to exhibit the opposite of that which is normal for you. As a result, you practically ensure your failure from the start by your own selection. Examples would include a timid man walking into a bar in which he knows he will get into a fight he can't win, a woman who is afraid of being assaulted walking alone at night in a dangerous part of the city, etc. More sophisticated examples would include any behaviour in which you are going out of your way to make life difficult for yourself by trying to be what you're not. You provoke precisely the kind of situations which are most painful for you and most destructive for your self-image and sense of well-being.

In stage four you may also exhibit predictable hysterical behaviour. You may construct situations unconsciously which permit you to alleviate your inner anxieties with hysterical outbursts and temper tantrums. You may experience fits of destructibility in which you do injury to property, yourself, or others. Or you may become super-impressionable, changing your fundamental beliefs from one day to the next, depending upon the persons and stimuli about you. All such behaviour is indicative of inner stresses which can no longer be contained and which seek external release.

3. THOUGHT

BEHAVIOUR

Chronic distortion of reality, over-personalizing events.

Alert to unspecificied danger; constant vigilance for "flaws" in things that seem right.

Suspicious, continually over-interprets insignificant pieces of information.

Deficiency in knowledge.

Repetitive, bothersome thoughts disrupt living.

Inability to experience specific feelings.

Difficulty in decision-making.

Explanation and Examples

Over-personalizing events is manifested when you interpret external events in terms of your own person. For instance, you may feel that whether your favourite sports team wins or loses is a reflection on your emotional participation as a television viewer. Or you may make a connection between the outbreak of a fire or a plane crash with some private personal thought or event. Alternatively, you may have a single explanatory system for all occurrences, such as astrology, in which you distort your perceptions of reality in order to conform to a single model of the universe. You may have a private code or explanation which enables you to make sense of inexplicable events.

A feeling of paranoia (that people, or events, are persecuting you) is also characteristic of neurotic characters. You are suspicious of yourself and others. You over-interpret insignificant events. You call someone up and he's not there and you interpret this to mean that he doesn't want to speak to you or that he doesn't like you. Or a friend fails to return your greeting in the street and you automatically assume he's trying to ignore you rather than assume that he merely didn't see you, which is probably the case.

Deficiency in knowledge means that you are blind to certain facts. You fail to gather sufficient information and are unaware of the gaps in your knowledge concerning both concrete situations and abstract relationships. You develop mental blocks which prevent you from utilizing your full range of problem-solving techniques. Even when these facts are pointed out, you are unable to understand or retain them.

You may have repetitive, bothersome thoughts which actually disrupt your work or your relationships. You may have continuous sexual fantasies which distract you completely from communicating with others. Religious thoughts, fears, or strong visual images may constantly impinge upon your thinking, making problem-solving or analytical thought impossible.

Your thoughts may so preoccupy you that specific feelings are completely blocked. You are unable to relate to another person with your full attention and strong emotions such as love, comradery, or anger fail to appear.

Perhaps the clearest indication of stage four thought behaviour is a total breakdown in your ability to make decisions. You have difficulty processing information. You go over the same facts again and again without analysing which factors you should concentrate on. You have difficulty in focusing on specific problems and issues. Your thinking goes round and round without advancing. Alternately, you finally do think a problem through, arriving at a good solution but abandon it in order to go through the process to arrive at another, and another, and another. You are full of doubts and always imagine that there is a better choice than those of which you are currently aware. You don't know when to *stop* gathering information. All decisions, even minor ones, seem of vital importance. In the end, you find yourself incapable of making a rational decision and act impulsively, later regretting the consequences and blaming yourself for not having stuck to your original choice of action.

4. ACTIVITY

BEHAVIOUR

Avoids new activities.
Activity no longer relieves tension.

Activities usually solitary, not engaged in lightly,
giving no particular pleasure in accomplishment; only pain/anxiety if not done.

Explanation and Examples

In stage four you avoid all new activities as far as
possible. You find mere survival taxing and feel that
your energies are tapped to the limit. You do not really
enjoy life or activities. They give you no sense of
competence, purpose, or meaning. You are frightened
that if you don't continue to go to work, talk to people,
or go out occasionally you will go completely mad, but
you do not experience positive satisfaction in your
accomplishments.

In every act, you see a life-and-death struggle. Every
defeat or failure is a sign that you are going under; your
successes are signs that you are still surviving. You
cannot afford to do something frivolously or lightly.
You must conserve your energy for important activities
because you feel you have so little of it. Your feeling of
doom or worthlessness is not alleviated by your activities.

5.   ORGANIZATION/CONTROL

BEHAVIOUR

Envies the machine.
Unexpected minor events cause work stoppage;
    ditto in love and play.
Obsessive rituals necessary to function.
Impulsive behaviour disrupts plans or relations;
    doesn't learn from experience.

Explanation and Examples

In stage four you would like to be able to treat
yourself like a machine, to be totally certain of always

making the same response and doing the same action. You envy the routine and total structure in which a machine operates — you know exactly what is expected of you and you don't have to cope with any human factors or uncertainties; you do not have to set your own pace or create your own work procedures; at least this is how you imagine your ideal work situation.

In your daily life, unexpected events completely throw you. A traffic delay, a detour, or getting lost all become major catastrophes accompanied by anxiety, anger, or temper displays. On a date you try to plan every detail and if anything goes wrong you become extremely anxious and consider the date spoiled. Other examples would include walking off the court in tennis when your partner fails to keep his proper position, going into a rage when finding a typing mistake in letters you dictated, or becoming morose, irritable, or angry upon learning that a film or sporting event you had planned on seeing is sold out. When such minor deviations not only bother you but destroy your sense of balance and ability to carry our or formulate plans, your behaviour is clearly neurotic.

In stage four you cannot tolerate any deviance. You try to plan every stage and event of your life. To protect yourself from variations or "mistakes" you develop set formulae for handling situations, people, and work projects. Often you need to go through extensive rituals in order to function. These rituals consist of idiosyncratic stylized behaviour. An example is the character played by Jack Nicholson in the film "Carnal Knowledge" in which he needs a call girl to recite a long speech praising him word by word in order to be able to have sex. In this case the film character is totally dependent upon a ritual in order to function. The use of rituals *per se* is not neurotic, but obsessive dependence upon them is.

Another possible sympton would be impulsive behaviour which disrupts plans. Again the clue is not impulsive behaviour itself which sometimes can be refreshing, but the disruptive effects of your impulses. You may painstakingly organize a system for retrieving information and then one day impulsively decide not to use it, throwing your files into chaos. A most important indicator of stage four would be the inability to learn from experience. If you make the same organizational errors again and again something is wrong. You should be able to modify your procedures and exercise sufficient self-control so as to improve upon your performance in work, love, and play. You are not able, in stage four, to avoid recreating negative environments or repeating inadequate responses.

6.   INTERPERSONAL

BEHAVIOUR

Continued withdrawal or aggression towards friends, causing some abandonment.
Extreme dependency and manipulation.
Extreme grudges.

Explanation and Examples

Your interpersonal problems are basically the same as those in stage three but more severe. You continue to withdraw from friends, either physically or emotionally. You think up excuses for avoiding colleagues and associates. If you go to a party you try to stay to the side, not involving yourself with others. An alternative, but similar manifestation, would be to exhibit extreme hostility when approached by others. In either case, you signal that you want to be left alone and this is generally the result achieved as some friends cease to associate with you.

In stage four you are extremely dependent upon a few key people. You feel that you can't live without them and will do anything to maintain their loyalty or their availability. Depending upon the personalities of those upon whom you are dependent, you may either be easily manipulated by them or find yourself manipulating them in order to maintain a hold upon them. Such manipulative behaviour creates strains in your relationships and they often break up in dramatic and sometimes violent confrontations. You do not easily forgive even minor betrayals and harbour permanent grudges.

7.   PHYSICAL

BEHAVIOUR

Stiffness and contraction in physical mannerisms.
Chronic psychosomatic problems — ulcers, colitis, insomnia, migraines, absence of periods, anorexia — IN ABSENCE OF CLEAR-CUT CAUSE.
Chronic solitary drug abuse as coping mechanism or self-medication.
Exhaustion.

Explanation and Examples

Physical mannerisms refer to voluntary and involuntary movements which are commonly performed such as walking, reaching, talking, eating, and the like. Walking with a heavy step, as if drugged, and stiffness and tightness in your muscles and body movements are examples.

Chronic psychosomatic problems refer to problems which have both a phsyical and mental component and which persist over long periods of time, longer than would be expected for solely physically-caused problems. All of the psychosomatic problems listed above may also occur normally as a result of specific external causes such as diet, drugs, and organic deterioration. However, when they occur inexplicably without a clearcut physical or environmental cause, they are probably signs of the extreme mental stress associated with stage four.

Ulcers usually form in the digestive tract of the stomach. They are extremely painful and are aggravated by certain diets of spicy or fatty foods, and by eating too fast. Colitis is an inflammation of the colon. It is painful to make bowel movements and may produce blood in your stools. Both these conditions should be treated by medical specialists.

Migraines are severe headaches which may persist for days and recur frequently. Insomnia is the inability to fall asleep. Absence of periods refers to a woman's failure to experience a normal menstrual flow. Anorexia refers to a prolonged lack of appetite. In severe cases, malnutrition and anaemia result. Extreme obesity and overeating would be comparable symptoms of stage four physical behaviour. Again, it should be recalled that a single neurotic character trait does not place you in stage four. This is especially true of physical symptoms which can often have other causes. Nonetheless, the presence of these symptoms is well worth investigating as a possible sign of mental illness.

Other physical traits include dependence on drugs for daily survival in response to mental and not physical conditions. This is especially true of drugs or alcohol which is taken alone and not in the company of others as a social act. Alcoholism and extreme drug abuse are associated with stage four.

Finally, sheer exhaustion, especially when not accompanied by perceivable mental or physical activity, is an important danger signal. Constant feelings of tiredness and exhaustion which are not linked to physical diseases are a sign of great interior mental stress and mental conflicts.

STAGE FIVE: PSYCHOTIC BEHAVIOUR AND CONDUCT DISORDERS

Stage five is that of major mental illnesses that should be treated as soon as possible. Stage five behaviour is that of lowest adaptability. People in stage five can no longer function adequately as members of society. Their inner conflicts consume all of their available energy and they have exhausted their strengths and positive resources for coping.

Within stage five there is probably as wide a range of behaviour variations as in the first four stages combined. Severe cases require hospitalization for rest and medical supervision of treatment. Milder problems could be dealt with in the home atmosphere.

General attributes of stage five behaviour include disruptive living patterns in all three spheres of life (work, love, and play), an inability to care for self, and gross distortions of reality or hallucinations. In stage five there is complete dependency on others. There is no stability. There are frequent and major breakdowns in all areas of life. There is not, as commonly exists in stage four, one saving area of competence and fulfilment which enables the individual to survive and to cope. You no longer see certain aspects of the world as those about you do and you have difficulty in communicating what you see and what you feel.

As a result, a common symptom of stage five behaviour is chronic conflict with parents, friends, school, and/or the law. You have special needs and are unable to adapt to the needs of others. You live in a world of your own with special dangers and rewards and when others impinge on these highly-charged and special domains you can no longer coordinate your behaviour with theirs.

In stage five you do things that other people consider "mad". You may see, hear, or feel things of which others aren't aware. You may experience feelings of private ecstasy which you are unable to communicate or control. You may believe that you are someone or something you're not. You may no longer perceive danger to your physical body, feeling that you have transcended yourself. You may expose yourself to dangers without realizing it, or attempt suicide (perhaps perceived by you as suicide against a part of your personality in order that an imagined new self may be born instead).

The list of possible disorders and manifestations of psychotic (mentally disordered) behaviour is endless. Particular perceptions may actually pertain to a higher realm of being or spirit above that of the everyday world. Real insights into significant extrasensory states may exist. Nonetheless, from the point of view of the everyday world these insights are too abstract or particular to be useful. The difference between being a madman and a genius is the ability to control and communicate. In stage five, you cannot control your behaviour; you cannot make others understand. The fault may lie in the imperfect state of society and the low level of reality at which man lives his everyday life, but in order to function in that everyday world it is necessary to be able to block out stimuli and to live within the confines of concrete action. Stage five persons are unable (not just unwilling) to do so.

Checklist for Psychotic Behaviour and Conduct Disorders

1. TENSION

BEHAVIOUR

Tension feels unbearable in absence of medication. Tension seems relieved only by psychotic thinking (distortion, hallucinations, grossly inappropriate plans).

Explanation and Examples

In stage five you often feel as if you're going to explode. Your anxieties enervate you. Neither work nor play nor any normal everyday activity relieves your tension. You can function only in response to drugs when experiencing these states of anxiety. Even frenetic behaviour — running around doing many tasks, taking care of many concerns which seem to be creating your anxieties — fails to help.

In addition to medication you may find yourself distorting reality in order to relieve tension. For example, if you are anxious about your inability to pay your bills you may convince yourself that you are going to receive a large inheritance from a nonexistent benefactor. You may also deal with unpleasant situations by imagining that they do not exist or that you have friends or voices which will come to your aid. Whenever you are tense these images, sights, or sounds will appear. Insofar as no one else can perceive these realities they are hallucinations.

Other psychotic thinking that may appear is the resolution of conflicts by grandiose or clearly inappropriate plans. Recorded cases include an unemployed guitarist writing to the Beatles for an audition and an acting student who planned on getting the lead role in a film that had already been made. A common manifestation is with regard to resolving failed interpersonal and romantic relationships by planning to establish an intimate relationship with some famous or far off figure whom you don't even know. In all cases, large miracle solutions and plans are made to deal with personal crises which you find yourself unable to accept or deal with in a practical and realistic fashion. Rather than admitting your inability and weaknesses, you make fantastic plans which serve as reassurances that you are a very special and successful individual. The plans are usually of such a nature that it is impossible even to begin to carry them out and failure to do so can be attributed to any number of external factors which do not reflect upon your own inadequacies and real conflicts and problems.

2. MOOD

BEHAVIOUR

Feelings unrelated to reality intermittently or chronically flood the individual.

Manic behaviour, frequently accompanied by delusions, ideas of reference, and distortions of reality.

Severely depressed mood brings halt to work or love; unreachable.

Thought disorders sometimes with hallucinations.

Explanation and Examples

In stage five, moods come upon you suddenly with no recognizable cause. Strong feelings surge from within and dominate your mood. These feelings are so strong that they counteract stimuli in the everyday world that normally account for your different moods.

Manic behaviour is that which is characterized by drastic changes in mood from one extreme of elation and hyperactivity to the opposite extreme of depression and inactivity. One moment you have high hopes, enthusiasm, and the feeling that you can't fail and hours later you are apathetic, sceptical, and fearful of embarrassing yourself. In most cases, both the elation and the depression are uncalled-for or inappropriate responses to what is actually going on around you. These responses are often accompanied by delusions (firmly held false beliefs). These delusions may be either paranoid (feeling persecuted or victimized), leading to depression, or protective (anonymous benefactor), leading to elation. An example of a delusion leading to manic behaviour would be the elated behaviour of a man who believed he was about to be given an important government post, although his actual occupation was that of a file clerk.

Ideas of reference and distortions of reality are

similar to delusions. Ideas of reference which are inappropriate are often associated with manic mood changes. For example, interpreting a song lyric as having been written or intended to explain your behaviour or that of someone close to you is a case of a misconceived point of reference. A distortion of reality is a milder form of a delusion. There is some basis for your beliefs but they are generally out of line: Your pretty co-worker actually does feel friendly toward you (though without the erotic overtones which you perceive); you may actually be eligible for an important government job, but at some later stage of your career.

In stage five, a depressed mood brings a total halt to your ability to work, love, or play. You are unable to enjoy yourself and your mood does not change even when that which you most want is offered or given to you. This may be true even when the situation or circumstance which produced your depression is totally removed. If you are depressed because you thought your girlfriend had left you for another and she hadn't, or because you had received an incorrect message concerning your financial position which is stronger than you had thought and you remain depressed after learning of these favourable events, you are suffering from depression. If all your friends try to cheer you up and can't; if no one seems able to relieve you of your problems or enable you to think of more pleasant subjects, then you would be psychologically unreachable and in need of professional guidance.

Severe depression and mood shifts are often associated with thought disorders and hallucinations. Hallucinations are sensory experiences not shared by others. They are produced by no stimuli, or stimuli which others do not perceive. As far as the rest of the world is concerned, you are seeing or hearing things. Hallucinations can be associated with your deep moods, insofar as your moods overwhelm your senses and heighten your experiences. For example, when elated you may be feeling so high that you see golden rays emanating from people you love. When depressed you may feel black beasts fighting in your gut and actually hear them shouting and struggling.

Thought disorders are cases of faulty thinking. Your positive or negative moods are so strong that you block out information which is incompatible with your present mood. You overlook facts and distort others as you are carried along by a single overpowering feeling or view of the world. In this state your thinking is often fuzzy and your judgment unreliable.

3.   THOUGHT

BEHAVIOUR

Obsessive thoughts.
Gross perceptual distortions.

Explanation and Examples

Stage five thought manifests itself in all of the disorders of stage four and more. Obsessive thoughts become frequent. Obsessive thoughts are those which you hold even when they are clearly inappropriate. They do not leave you alone; you cannot get them out of your mind. Certain questions, ideas, or desires may become obsessive. You can become obsessed with the idea of writing a book, of making love to a certain woman, or of solving the riddle of the meaning of life. In all three cases it is a good bet that your obsessive thought is either an impossible desire or a goal toward which you make no constructive effort. You always think of writing a best-seller but never actually sit down and write at all. The woman you want to make love to is married to a famous actor and lives two thousand miles away. It is impossible to solve the riddle of the meaning of life. Curiosity or mild concern with such thoughts from time to time would not be abnormal. What *is* abnormal is the intensity with which stage five psychotics cling to such thoughts. They never stop contemplating the same issues over and over again. They become oblivious to other people and other ideas and are unable to redirect their energies, thoughts, and desires to other, more easily obtainable subjects and goals.

Insofar as they are unable to satisfy their desires in the everyday world they retreat further and further into a private fantasy world in which their desires are fulfilled. This may result in gross perceptual distortions. Their psyches can no longer tolerate the continual barrage on their private fantasy world that contact with the "real" world produces. To deal with this conflict between their perceptions of the world with their eyes, ears, and other senses and the idealized world of thoughts and fantasies they carry within, they begin to resort to distortions. They no longer see what they don't want to see. They distort images so that they will agree with their private vision of how the world ought to be. Sometimes this private "ought" world can be terrifying and painful. Yet the realization that the world is not as the psychotic imagines may be more terrifying still. It is important to point out that such perceptual distortions are usually quite specific. For the most part the psychotic thinks and perceives as well as any normal person. He is not retarded. There are certain key areas in which his perceptions and thinking processes break down. These areas are those which are in conflict with obsessive thoughts, and with his private fantasy world. For every psychotic, these areas will be different and unique and ultimately they will correspond with real problems and conflicts which have produced these fantasy worlds.

4.   ACTIVITY

BEHAVIOUR

Compulsive ritualistic activity.
Extreme difficulty in changing patterns of activity.

Explanation and Examples

Compulsive ritualistic activity is that which is repeated over and over again despite its inappropriateness or lack of connection to reality. The activity is rigid and totally self-contained. It may start as a normal desire for hygiene and cleanliness and end as ritualistic hand-washing which is performed a hundred or more times a day. In stage five, these rituals no longer facilitate work or reduce tension. They have become an end in themselves and an obsession. You feel that you cannot rest until a certain rite is performed but no sooner are you finished than you begin to prepare yourself to start your ritualistic behaviour all over again.

In stage five, whatever activity patterns you may have come to follow are extremely difficult to change. This includes activity which is normal. You need a very definite routine. When your routine is disrupted you are frightened that your worst moods and compulsions will overcome you. You have no desire to take on new activities, and although you may be very unhappy, you feel that the goal is to repeat the acts of yesterday, for in this way at least things won't get worse. In stage five, this reluctance to engage in new activities is severe. Safe and obviously enjoyable new opportunities such as dinner invitations, parties, and trips are turned down because of your uneasiness in deviating from set motions and activities. You are at the lowest level of adaptability and cannot even adapt to positive changes in your environment.

5.   ORGANIZATION/CONTROL

BEHAVIOUR

Little self-control; easily influenced by suggestion or internal feelings.

Feelings indicate when and if work is possible.

Impulsive behaviour expected.

Explanation and Examples

In stage five, you have little self-control. In severe psychotic states you have none; not even control over your evacuatory movements and basic bodily functions. In less severe cases you will retain some self-control, but are easily influenced and directed by outside stimuli and uncontrollable inner feelings. You may still be able to initiate a project you want to work on and you enjoy doing but will be unable to continue if someone suggests that you should stop and do something else. You have no confidence in your plans and lose a sense of your self. You react to moods and other people's desires and are unable to follow through on activities or ideas.

In order to accomplish anything, the setting must be just right. You must be feeling in the right mood, the weather must be perfect, your friends must also be in the same mood, and you must have the perfect ingredients in order to enjoy a garden party, for example. The same perfect conditions are necessary for successful work and lovemaking. Since these perfect conditions seldom exist, you withdraw from many activities. The most important ingredients are your mood and your inner feelings. Since these are seldom just right for the occasion, you begin to shape the occasion to them. The result is impulsive behaviour, directed and dictated by your moods and feelings. No one, including yourself, knows what mood you are going to be in. No one can predict your behaviour and you act without regard to the appropriateness of the situation or the feelings of others. Since conditions are never perfect, you abandon concern with any but internal factors and become oblivious to the outside world. In stage four, such impulsive behaviour can be disruptive to self and others. In stage five, it almost always is.

6. INTERPERSONAL

BEHAVIOUR

Autism.
Sociopathic behaviour.

Explanation and Examples

Autism is a psychlogical term which refers to the inability of an individual to relate to external stimuli. Examples of autistic behaviour are the inability to talk, the inability to engage in social behaviour, or the response to stimuli which others can't perceive. Autism is the absorption in fantasy as an escape from reality. In the interpersonal sphere this produces a breakdown of social relationships. The autistic individual does not respond to others as they are, but as he imagines them in his fantasies. An autistic individual may persist in amorous advances to a woman who has clearly rejected him on many occasions. In more severe cases of autism, communication breaks down entirely and no one is able to understand acts and movements which take on a bizarre unique aspect.

Sociopathic behaviour is extreme anti-social behaviour. Such behaviour is characteristic of individuals who will stop at nothing to satisfy their needs and desires. They show no concern for others or for conventional morality and do not experience guilt feelings even after blatantly and ruthlessly hurting relatives or friends. As a consequence, they seldom maintain friendships for long and are often loners. The dominant theme in interpersonal relationships for the sociopath is hostility. This hostility may take many forms and is characterized by a total disregard for the presence and feelings of others. Examples of sociopathic behaviour include habitual lying, stealing, cheating and physical attacks against others. In stage five, such anti-social behaviour is not modified even in the face of negative feedback. For example, a man who constantly lies, whose lies are found out, who is subsequently punished for his lies, and who in the face of severe punishments, legal action, and ostracism by his friends continues to lie, displays sociopathic behaviour. More serious cases include harassment of neighbours, physical assaults, violent robberies and, in the most extreme case, murder.

7.   PHYSICAL

BEHAVIOUR

Bizarre physical posturing.
Many physical problems.
Addictions.

Explanation and Examples

Bizarre physical posturing refers to staring and hand, leg, or body trunk movements which are clearly strange and out of the ordinary. For example, constant intense staring which is not modified in the face of normal social constraints is bizarre behaviour. Tight muscles and always standing at a severe angle as if on the verge of falling down would be another example of bizarre physical posturing. Any deviance in normal body control which is not the result of a physical abnormality would be included in stage five physical behaviour.

Many physical problems include all of those listed in stage four and others. Stage five individuals generally don't feel well physically, adopt lifestyles which are not conducive to sound physical health, are accident-prone, and take a long time to recover from normal illnesses. The precise relationship between physical and mental problems is still unknown, but scientists are discovering ever greater feedback mechanisms between physical and mental factors, including the relationship between hormone production and chemical processes and emotional states and behaviour syndromes.

Finally, outright addictions are signs of psychotic physical behaviour. These addictions may take different forms, from addiction to alcohol and everyday aspirin to heroin. The point about addictions is that they are signals of a complete breakdown in control over your physical person. You are dependent upon certain substances and your body can't function without them. An addicted individual has reached the lowest level of adaptability, because he is incapable of adapting to any environment in which the substance to which he is addicted is absent.

4

HOW TO USE
THE DIAGNOSTIC CHECKLISTS
AND MENTAL HEALTH
SELF EVALUATION CHART

The theory, system of classification, and the nature of the symptoms used to diagnose mental health explained so far need to be fully understood before you can use the diagnostic checklists to test your own mental health.

The diagnostic test consists of seven mini-charts, corresponding to each of the seven characteristics of mental behaviour. Each mini-chart lists all the possible behaviour patterns and symptoms that correspond to each of the five stages of mental adaptability. You simply tick off those behaviour patterns and symptoms which most accurately and honestly characterize your feelings and actions for each of the seven areas of behaviour.

This marking off alone will give you a mini-picture of your state of mental health for each of the seven characteristics. Then, with the aid of the point score system you can calculate a total score for each sub-area; this can be transferred to the Self-Evaluation chart on page 120 which will be used to diagnose your overall mental health. Examples are provided after each mini-chart for the calculation of your point scores and four hypothetical mental health Self-Evaluation charts are also included, with full explanations.

Two important reminders: It is expected that your behaviour for each of the seven characteristics will include symptoms from different stages of mental health. Do not be alarmed if your behaviour includes symptoms from each of the five stages of mental health from normal to severe disorder. Given the complex and varied nature of mental health, such an occurrence is not impossible. The chart is devised so that these apparent contradictions will be dealt with through the use of the point scores in the preparation of your overall mental health visual Self-Evaluation chart.

The second reminder: If you do not understand a symptom or behaviour pattern, do not guess or leave it blank. Go back to the text in which each symptom was first presented in the context of the stage of mental health to which it corresponds. The diagnostic mini-charts are especially designed to facilitate such cross-checking. Look across the page to see what stage of mental health corresponds to the puzzling or only partially understood symptom. Then turn to that chapter and read down until you come to the symptom in question and the full explanation which accompanies it. All terms used in the diagnostic charts are fully explained in the text and have been carefully organized to facilitate immediate recognition. Such cross-checking is essential if you are to avoid guessing and achieve an accurate diagnosis of your mental health.

Please turn over for first diagnostic chart.

DIAGNOSTIC CHART   Characteristic 1: Tension

BEHAVIOUR AND SYMPTOMS

1. Tension has cause in the present or past.
2. Can do something that helps.

3. Clear-cut signs of tension (agitation, rapid breathing, sweating).
4. Tension may or may not inhibit work.

5. Signs of tension with no apparent cause.
6. Tension inhibits work (most of the time).

7. Dependent on strong defences to make tension bearable.
8. Periods of nearly unbearable anxiety with no obvious cause.

9. Tension feels unbearable in absence of medication.
10. Tension only relieved by psychotic thinking (distortions, hallucinations, grossly inappropriate plans).

	NORMAL	EMERGENCY	NEUROTIC COPING	NEUROTIC CHARACTER	SEVERE DISORDER
1.	☐				
2.	☐				
3.		☐			
4.		☐			
5.			☐		
6.			☐		
7.				☐	
8.				☐	
9.					☐
10.					☐

TICK THE BOXES WHICH CORRESPOND TO YOUR TENSION BEHAVIOUR. YOUR BEHAVIOUR MAY FALL INTO SEVERAL STAGES OF MENTAL HEALTH.

To Calculate Point Score for Tension Behaviour

SYMPTOM	POINTS	YOUR SCORE	WORK SPACE
1	10		
2	10		
3	20		
4	20		
5	30		
6	30		
7	40		
8	40		
9	50		
10	50		

Total score _____ divided by the number of symptoms recorded _____ equals Tension point score. [_____].

Fill in the number of points for each symptom you marked off in the "Tension" diagnostic chart on the preceding page. Add up your total score for this characteristic, writing the total in the space provided. Now add up the number of symptoms (this will be a number between 1 and 10) and write this number beneath your total score. Divide the total score by the number of symptoms reported. The result is your score for mental adaptability as measured by TENSION behaviour. Record this number in the box provided and refer to it when you have completed your self-diagnosis and are ready to calculate your overall mental health adaptability score (at which stage you transfer it on to the mental health visual Self-Evaluation chart on page 120).

Example: If you ticked TENSION symptoms 1, 2, 3, 6, and 9:

1	10
2	10
3	20
6	30
9	50
120	Total score
5	Number of symptoms

A total score of 120 divided by 5 symptoms equals a Tension point score of 24.

The procedure for the next six mini-charts is the same. Be sure you understand each symptom before using these checklists.

DIAGNOSTIC CHART   Characteristic 2: Mood

BEHAVIOUR AND SYMPTOMS

1. Mood swings have cause.
2. Presence of humour.
3. Moods can be intense but pass within short time.

4. Sense of being easily upset, moody, intolerant.
5. Explosive humour as tension release.

6. Moods last for long periods.
7. Intermittent hysterical behaviour.
8. Hyper-emotional expressions without awareness.
9. Hostile wit.
10. Mild chronic fears and phobias.
11. Counterphobic behaviour with some risk.
12. Blocked specific emotions.

13. Background moods affect work, love, play.
14. Chronic depressed, unhappy states.
15. Suicide attempts.
16. Get "high" on ideas but problems in following through.
17. Self-destructive counterphobic acting out.
18. Predictable hysterical behaviour.

19. Delusions, thought disorders, or hallucinations.
20. Severe depression, unreachable, complete halt to work or love.

NORMAL	EMERGENCY	NEUROTIC COPING	NEUROTIC CHARACTER	SEVERE DISORDER
1. ☐				
2. ☐				
3. ☐				
	4. ☐			
	5. ☐			
		6. ☐		
		7. ☐		
		8. ☐		
		9. ☐		
		10. ☐		
		11. ☐		
		12. ☐		
			13. ☐	
			14. ☐	
			15. ☐	
			16. ☐	
			17. ☐	
			18. ☐	
				19. ☐
				20. ☐

TICK THE BOXES WHICH CORRESPOND TO YOUR MOOD BEHAVIOUR. YOUR BEHAVIOUR MAY FALL INTO SEVERAL STAGES OF MENTAL HEALTH.

To Calculate Point Score for Mood Behaviour

SYMPTOM	POINTS	YOUR SCORE	WORK SPACE
1	10		
2	10		
3	10		
4	20		
5	20		
6	30		
7	30		
8	30		
9	30		
10	30		
11	30		
12	30		
13	40		
14	40		
15	40		
16	40		
17	40		
18	40		
19	50		
20	50		

Total score _____ divided by the number of symptoms recorded _____ equals Mood point score. ☐

Fill in the number of points for each symptom you ticked off in the "Mood" diagnostic chart on the preceding page. Add up your total score for this characteristic, writing the total in the space provided. Now add up the number of symptoms (this will be a number between 1 and 20) and write this number beneath your total score. Divide the total score by the number of symptoms reported. The result is your score for mental adaptability as measured by MOOD behaviour. Record this number in the box and refer to it when you have completed your self-diagnosis and are ready to calculate your overall mental health adaptability score (at which stage you transfer it to the visual Self-Evaluation chart on page 120).

Example: If you ticked MOOD symptoms 1, 2, 3, 4, 5, 6, 7, 10, 13, 14, and 16:

1	10
2	10
3	10
4	20
5	20
6	30
7	30
10	30
13	40
14	40
16	40
280	Total score
11	Number of symptoms

A total score of 280 divided by 11 symptoms equals a Mood point score of 25.5.

DIAGNOSTIC CHART   Characteristic 3: Thought

Behaviour and Symptoms

1. Able to secure and process information.
2. Thoughts of whatever kind do not upset for long.
3. Thoughts facilitate action.

4. Thoughts intensely, narrowly focused on task or problem.
5. Tension release through thoughts — passive, aggressive, sexual.
6. Selective inattention.

7. Tendency to analyse rather than experience feelings.
8. Questions ability to feel important emotions.
9. Circular worrying.

10. Chronic distortions of reality.
11. Alert to unspecified danger.
12. Deficiency in knowledge.
13. Repetitive, bothersome thoughts disrupt living.
14. Inability to experience specific feelings.
15. Inability to make decisions.

16. Obsessive thoughts.
17. Gross perceptual distortions.

		NEUROTIC	NEUROTIC	SEVERE
NORMAL	EMERGENCY	COPING	CHARACTER	DISORDER

1. ☐
2. ☐
3. ☐

4. ☐

5. ☐
6. ☐

7. ☐
8. ☐
9. ☐

10. ☐
11. ☐
12. ☐
13. ☐
14. ☐
15. ☐

16. ☐
17. ☐

TICK THE BOXES WHICH CORRESPOND TO YOUR
THOUGHT BEHAVIOUR. YOUR BEHAVIOUR MAY FALL
INTO SEVERAL STAGES OF MENTAL HEALTH.

To Calculate Point Score for Thought Behaviour

SYMPTOM	POINTS	YOUR SCORE	WORK SPACE
1	10		
2	10		
3	10		
4	20		
5	20		
6	20		
7	30		
8	30		
9	30		
10	40		
11	40		
12	40		
13	40		
14	40		
15	40		
16	50		
17	50		

Total score _____ divided by the number of symptoms recorded _____ equals Thought point score. [   ]

Fill in the number of points for each symptom you ticked off in the "Thought" diagnostic chart on the preceding page. Add up your total score for this characteristic, writing the total in the space provided. Add up the number of symptoms (this will be a number between 1 and 17). Divide the total score by the number of symptoms reported. The result is your score for mental adaptability as measured by THOUGHT behaviour. Record this number ready for transfer as explained under the first two diagnostic charts.

Example: If you ticked THOUGHT symptoms 1, 2, 3, 4, 6, 9, 13, and 15:

1	10
2	10
3	10
4	20
6	20
9	30
13	40
15	40
	180 Total score
	8 Number of symptoms

A total score of 180 divided by 8 symptoms equals a Thought Point score of 22.5.

DIAGNOSTIC CHART   Characteristic 4: Activity

BEHAVIOUR AND SYMPTOMS

1. Enthusiasm and interest in doing, participating, bringing sense of competence.
2. Risk-taking and resilience — daring to be mediocre or fail and try again.
3. Activity may be uneven or continuous.

4. According to temperament, lots of activity or little.
5. Anxiety about new risks or overload.
6. Talismanic words, behaviour.

7. Hyperactivity with no point.
8. Needs inspiration or feedback to work adequately.
9. Marked reduction in risk-taking.

10. Avoids new activities.
11. Activity no longer relieves tension.
12. Activities solitary, no pleasure in accomplishing, pain if not done.

13. Compulsive ritualistic activity.
14. Extreme difficulty in changing patterns of activity.

| | | NEUROTIC | NEUROTIC | SEVERE |
| NORMAL | EMERGENCY | COPING | CHARACTER | DISORDER |

1. ☐

2. ☐
3. ☐

    4. ☐
    5. ☐
    6. ☐

        7. ☐
        8. ☐
        9. ☐

            10. ☐
            11. ☐

            12. ☐

                13. ☐
                14. ☐

TICK THE BOXES WHICH CORRESPOND TO YOUR ACTI-
VITY BEHAVIOUR. YOUR BEHAVIOUR MAY FALL INTO
SEVERAL STAGES OF MENTAL HEALTH.

To Calculate Point Score for Activity Behaviour

SYMPTOM	POINTS	YOUR SCORE	WORK SPACE
1	10		
2	10		
3	10		
4	20		
5	20		
6	20		
7	30		
8	30		
9	30		
10	40		
11	40		
12	40		
13	50		
14	50		

Total score _____ divided by the number of symptoms recorded _____ equals Activity point score. [   ]

Fill in the number of points for each symptom you ticked. Add up your total score for this characteristic. Add up the number of symptoms (between 1 and 14). Divide the total score by the number of symptoms. The result is your score for mental adaptability as measured by ACTIVITY behaviour. Record in the box provided, ready for transfer to page 120 as explained before.

Example: If you ticked ACTIVITY symptoms 1, 2, 3, 4, 8, and 10:

1	10
2	10
3	10
4	20
8	30
10	40
120	Total score
6	Number of symptoms

A total score of 120 divided by 6 symptoms equals an Activity point score of 20.

DIAGNOSTIC CHART   Characteristic 5: Organization/Control

BEHAVIOUR AND SYMPTOMS

1. Can sit still and address self to task for increasingly long periods.
2. Can work in absence of inspiration or feedback.
3. Plan and carry out solutions to multi-step problems.
4. Learn from experience.
5. Freedom to use behavioural repertoire flexibly.

6. Anxiety stimulates action.
7. May lie or cheat under pressure.

8. Increased rigidity: desires clear-cut demands and perfect conditions to function.
9. Chronic condition of being over-extended.
10. Unpredictable events disrupt performance badly.
11. Occasional impulsive behaviour.
12. Rituals interfere with work.
13. Limited capacity for self-generated insight and change.

14. Envies the machine.
15. Unexpected minor events cause work stoppage; ditto in love and play.
16. Obsessive rituals necessary to function.

17. Impulsive behaviour disrupts plans; doesn't learn from experience.
18. Little self-control; easily influenced by suggestion or internal feelings.
19. Feelings dictate when and if work is possible.
20. Impulsive behaviour expected.

	NORMAL	EMERGENCY	NEUROTIC COPING	NEUROTIC CHARACTER	SEVERE DISORDER
1.	☐				
2.	☐				
3.	☐				
4.	☐				
5.	☐				
6.		☐			
7.		☐			
8.			☐		
9.			☐		
10.			☐		
11.			☐		
12.			☐		
13.			☐		
14.				☐	
15.				☐	
16.				☐	
17.				☐	
18.					☐
19.					☐
20.					☐

TICK THE BOXES WHICH CORRESPOND TO YOUR ORGANI-
ZATION/CONTROL BEHAVIOUR. YOUR BEHAVIOUR MAY
FALL INTO SEVERAL STAGES OF MENTAL HEALTH.

To Calculate Point Score for Organization/Control behaviour

SYMPTOM	POINTS	YOUR SCORE	WORK SPACE
1	10		
2	10		
3	10		
4	10		
5	10		
6	20		
7	20		
8	30		
9	30		
10	30		
11	30		
12	30		
13	30		
14	40		
15	40		
16	40		
17	40		
18	50		
19	50		
20	50		

Total score _____ divided by the number of symptoms recorded _____ equals Organization/Control point score. [   ]

Fill in the number of points for each symptom you ticked. Add up your total. Add up the number of symptoms (between 1 and 20). Divide the total score by the number of symptoms reported. The result is your score for mental adaptability as measured by ORGANIZATION/CONTROL behaviour. Record as before.

Example: If you ticked ORGANIZATION/CONTROL symptoms 3, 4, 5, 7, 8, 10, 11, and 18:

3	10
4	10
5	10
7	20
8	30
10	30
11	30
18	<u>50</u>
	190 Total score
	8 Number of symptoms

A total score of 190 divided by 8 symptoms equals an Organization/Control point score of 23.75.

DIAGNOSTIC CHART Characteristic 6: Interpersonal

Behaviour and Symptoms

1. Be a friend as well as having friends.
2. Increasing capacity for intimacy.
3. Withdrawal or aggression have clear causes and pass.

4. Can use upset feelings manipulatively to seek attention.
5. Anxiety about pleasing others.
6. Unwillingness or inability to "play".
7. Over-emotional in interpersonal relationships.
8. Irritability.

9. Moving towards, against, or away from others in overdriven manner.
10. Must always get own way, inability to compromise.
11. Can be scapegoated or bullyish.
12. Prematurely initiate one-to-one relationships.
13. Changing, deteriorating friendships often featured by grudges.
14. Need constant external support.
15. Low self-esteem.
16. Mild anti-social behaviour or alientation.

17. Extreme dependency and/or manipulation.
18. Extreme grudges.

19. Autism.
20. Sociopathic behaviour.

	NORMAL	EMERGENCY	NEUROTIC COPING	NEUROTIC CHARACTER	SEVERE DISORDER
1.	☐				
2.	☐				
3.	☐				
4.		☐			
5.		☐			
6.		☐			
7.		☐			
8.		☐			
9.			☐		
10.			☐		
11.			☐		
12.			☐		
13.			☐		
14.			☐		
15.			☐		
16.			☐		
17.				☐	
18.				☐	
19.					☐
20.					☐

TICK THE BOXES WHICH CORRESPOND TO YOUR INTER-PERSONAL BEHAVIOUR. YOUR BEHAVIOUR MAY FALL INTO SEVERAL STAGES OF MENTAL HEALTH.

To Calculate Point Score for Interpersonal Behaviour

SYMPTOM	POINTS	YOUR SCORE	WORK SPACE
1	10		
2	10		
3	10		
4	20		
5	20		
6	20		
7	20		
8	20		
9	30		
10	30		
11	30		
12	30		
13	30		
14	30		
15	30		
16	30		
17	40		
18	40		
19	50		
20	50		

Total score _____ divided by the number of symptoms recorded _____ equals Interpersonal point score. [_____]

Fill in the number of points for each symptom you ticked. Add up your total score. Add up the number of symptoms (between 1 and 20). Divide the total score by the number of symptoms reported. The result is your score for mental adaptability as measured by INTER-PERSONAL behaviour. Record as before.

Example: If you ticked INTERPERSONAL symptoms 1, 2, 3, 5, 7, 15, and 18:

1	10
2	10
3	10
5	20
7	20
15	30
18	40
140	Total score
7	Number of symptoms

A total score of 140 divided by 7 symptoms equals an Interpersonal point score of 20.

DIAGNOSTIC CHART   Characteristic 7: Physical

BEHAVIOUR AND SYMPTOMS

1. Stability of GI system, skin, breathing, sleep, weight.
2. Relatively quick recovery from illness/accident.
3. Sense of feeling well.

4. Fluctuations in eating and sleeping patterns, weight, minor GI problems, skin blemishes.
5. Physical sensations of tension, tiredness, or using up physical reserves.
6. Conscious use of drugs to cope.

7. Intermittent skin, GI problems, obesity, lack of appetite, sleep disturbances, headaches.
8. Physical tics, stuttering.
9. Complaints about health with no plainly defined symptoms.
10. Seeks drugs/medical help to "feel better".
11. Episodic drug abuse, socially reinforced.

12. Stiffness and contraction in physical mannerisms.
13. Chronic psychosomatic problems — ulcers, colitis, insomnia, migraines, absence of periods, anorexia — without clear-cut cause.
14. Chronic solitary drug abuse as coping mechanism or self-medication.
15. Exhaustion.

16. Bizarre physical posturing.
17. Many physical problems.
18. Addictions.

NORMAL	EMERGENCY	NEUROTIC COPING	NEUROTIC CHARACTER	SEVERE DISORDER
1. ☐				
2. ☐				
3. ☐				
	4. ☐			
	5. ☐			
	6. ☐			
		7. ☐		
		8. ☐		
		9. ☐		
		10. ☐		
		11. ☐		
			12. ☐	
			13. ☐	
			14. ☐	
			15. ☐	
				16. ☐
				17. ☐
				18. ☐

TICK THE BOXES WHICH CORRESPOND TO YOUR PHYSICAL BEHAVIOUR. YOUR BEHAVIOUR MAY FALL INTO SEVERAL STAGES OF MENTAL HEALTH.

To Calculate Point Score for Physical Behaviour

SYMPTOM	POINTS	YOUR SCORE	WORK SPACE
1	10		
2	10		
3	10		
4	20		
5	20		
6	20		
7	30		
8	30		
9	30		
10	30		
11	30		
12	40		
13	40		
14	40		
15	40		
16	50		
17	50		
18	50		

Total score _____ divided by the number of symptoms recorded _____ equals Physical point score. [   ]

Fill in the number of points for each symptom you ticked. Add up your total score. Add up the number of symptoms (between 1 and 18). Divide the total score by the number of symptoms reported. The result is your score for mental adaptability as measured by PHYSICAL behaviour. Record as before.

Example: If you ticked PHYSICAL symptoms 1, 2, 4, and 5:

1	10
2	10
4	20
5	20
60	Total score
4	Number of symptoms

A total score of 60 dived by 4 symptoms equals a Physical point score of 15.

MENTAL HEALTH SELF-EVALUATION CHART 1

Once you have computed your total scores for each of the seven characteristics you will be able to fill in the chart overleaf with a picture of your mental health. Simply shade in the area for each characteristic which lies to the left of your point score. The result is a visual image of your present state of mental health. Four examples, complete with charts, are provided in the section on "Interpretation and Self-Evaluation" which immediately follows.

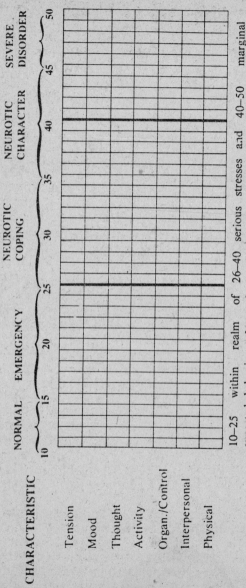

SELF-EVALUATION CHART I

POINTS

CHARACTERISTIC	NORMAL	EMERGENCY	NEUROTIC COPING	NEUROTIC CHARACTER	SEVERE DISORDER
	10 15	20 25	30 35	40	45 50
Tension					
Mood					
Thought					
Activity					
Organ./Control					
Interpersonal					
Physical					

10–25 within realm of expected behaviour. Normal functioning. May want help with specific problems, i.e. preventive therapy.

26–40 serious stresses and problems. Professional help may be advisable. Functioning with difficulty.

40–50 marginal functioning. Seek formal help.

Interpretation

For general interpretive ease, your point scores and Self-Evaluation chart can be broken down to one of three possible categories. An average score in the 10 to 25 point range is within the realm of expected normal behaviour and normal functioning. You may want help with specific problems and, as with most people, you could probably benefit from preventive therapy, but you have no serious mental problems at this time and have a high level of mental adaptability.

If your average score is in the 26 to 40 point range you are functioning but with difficulty. You have serious stresses and problems, and professional help is probably advisable.

An average score in the 40 to 50 point range indicates marginal functioning and is a clear call to seek formal help.

Once again, you should be reminded that your mental health changes over time, as does your physical health. Whatever category of mental adaptability you may be in today is not necessarily a permanent definition of your mental being. At the same time, as with your physical health, you should be aware that your mental health is more likely to deteriorate than to improve if health problems are left untreated or ignored. A healthy environment or positive intervention will promote your mental health, as will a negative environment or negative intervention lower your level of health and adaptability.

Self-Evaluation

The chart or pictograph gives you a picture of your mental health. It tells you which areas of behaviour give you problems, the degree to which they are problems, and the areas in which you are functioning well. Note that very few scores will fall in either the normal category of 10 to 15 points, or the severe disorder category of 45 to 50 points. The vast majority of scores and people are somewhere in between. They have mental problems of varying degrees, but are still able to function.

Depending upon your mental health pictograph scores, the state of your mental health may be obvious at a glance or, for borderline cases, you may need a more precise point evaluation. The calculation of an exact point average score is possible. Merely add up your point scores for each of the seven characteristics and divide by 7 as in the examples below.

Sample Scores, Interpretation, and Discussion

CASE ONE: BORDERLINE NORMAL

MENTAL HEALTH CHART

POINT SCORES		NORMAL		DIFFICULTIES	MARGINAL
		10 15 20 25	30 35 40	45 50	
Tension	24				
Mood	19				
Thought	27				
Activity	16				
Organ./Control	10				
Interpersonal	30				
Physical	42				
Total score	168				
divide by 7 = 24 average score.					

THE PICTURE SHOWS, AS DOES THE POINT SCORE, THAT THIS IS CLEARLY A BORDERLINE NORMAL STATE OF MENTAL HEALTH.

INTERPRETATION: Case one exhibits minor problems in tension behaviour, minimal problems with regard to mood and activity, and excellent organization/control behaviour. There are major problems in thought and interpersonal behaviour and extremely serious physical problems. Given the fact that, except for physical behaviour, no other category exceeds neurotic coping behaviour, case one is best regarded as borderline normal. It would be wise to investigate the physical problems, which in this case, would appear to be caused as much by the physical as the mental factors. The excellent organization/control score indicates strong inner reserves, self-discipline, and the capacity to overcome your problems.

SUGGESTIONS: Seek attention for physical problems. As a minimum, have a physical check-up, watch diet, and follow a routine of regular exercise. For interpersonal problems seek informal counselling.

CASE TWO: EXTREMELY ADAPTABLE

MENTAL HEALTH CHART

POINT SCORES		NORMAL		DIFFICULTIES		MARGINAL
		10 15 20	25 30 35	40	45 50	
Tension	15					
Mood	10					
Thought	10					
Activity	15					
Organ./Control	10					
Interpersonal	12					
Physical	18					
Total score	90					

divided by 7 = 12.9
average score.

THE PICTURE SHOWS: AS DOES THE POINT SCORE: THAT THIS IS CLEARLY A NORMAL STATE OF MENTAL HEALTH.

INTERPRETATION: An enviable score. No major mental problems. Some minor physical problems, an occasional symptom in tension behaviour and activities.

SUGGESTIONS: Keep living as you are. You are very fortunate.

CASE THREE: MAJOR MENTAL HEALTH PROBLEMS

MENTAL HEALTH CHART

POINT SCORES		NORMAL			DIFFICULTIES		MARGINAL	
		10 15 20	25	30 35	40	45 50		
Tension	35							
Mood	25							
Thought	25							
Activity	40							
Organ./Control	33							
Interpersonal	45							
Physical	35							
Total score	238							

divided by 7 = 34
average score.

THE PICTURE SHOWS: AS DOES THE POINT SCORE: THAT THIS IS CLEARLY A CASE OF MAJOR MENTAL HEALTH PROBLEMS, BORDERING BETWEEN STAGE THREE NEUROTIC COPING STYLES AND STAGE FOUR NEUROTIC CHARACTER.

INTERPRETATION: This is a clear case in which intervention would be advised. There are particularly severe interpersonal problems which should receive immediate attention. All areas are subject to problems, although mood and thought behaviour are still more or less under control. A person with this score is still functioning but with great difficulties.

SUGGESTIONS: Seek some form of professional guidance. Your problems are more than those normally encountered. Treat them now while they are still amenable to treatment before they get worse.

CASE FOUR: NORMAL WITH MINOR PROBLEMS

MENTAL HEALTH CHART

POINT SCORES		NORMAL			DIFFICULTIES		MARGINAL	
		10 15 20	25	30 35	40	45 50		
Tension	15							
Mood	22							
Thought	20							
Activity	20							
Organ./Control	24							
Interpersonal	20							
Physical	15							
Total score	136							

divided by 7 = 19.4
average score.

THE PICTURE SHOWS: AS DOES THE POINT SCORE: THAT THIS IS A CASE OF A NORMAL PERSON WITH MANY MINOR MENTAL HEALTH PROBLEMS.

INTERPRETATION: A point score of 19.4 indicates a person within the range of normal, but approximating to stage two, emergency behaviour. If real emergencies exist, these symptoms are perfectly normal and the external factors should be altered, rather than the subject be treated. If external conditions are normal and no emergencies exist, then these symptoms may indicate more significant mental problems and should receive treatment. General mental health is good, but care should be taken in terms of mood and organization/control behaviour. The organization/control score indicates problems in self-control and self-discipline and is a probable danger signal indicating a need for at least informal attention to this aspect of your life.

SUGGESTIONS: Depending upon other factors no immediate action is necessry. If you have misgivings about the direction of your life you might seek enrichment or preventive therapy in some form (anything from transcendental meditation to an encounter group, in accordance with your personality). Most people with this score, however, are merely suffering from the normal stresses and difficulties of daily living in an imperfect world. You have problems, but they are not interfering with normal functioning.

5

WHERE DO YOU GO WHEN YOU'RE IN TROUBLE?

There is no easy answer to this question. Where to go depends upon your family, your economic resources, your values, and general features of your personality such as age, educational background, and sex. It also depends, perhaps most specifically, on the degree of mental trouble you have diagnosed with the aid of this book.

There are, however, five general areas in which to seek help, namely, (1) personal resources, (2) your own Doctor, (3) private non-medical counselling services, (4) provincial or city medical clinics and facilities of the public health service, and (5) private medical practice.

Your best resource in times of trouble is yourself. Draw on your friends, your skills, and your interests to help you get through difficult periods. Merely confiding in friends and discussing your problems with them can help you get your problems into the open. In addition, the sympathy and advice of friends can at least give you a "cushion" for a time, to decide if it is necessary to seek other forms of help. The majority of people with mental problems handle depressions in this way. Often neurotic problems are time-limited, or the result of particular transitional situations such as job changes, marriages, deaths, and divorces which pass, and in passing remove the stresses which are causing the neurotic difficulties.

Even more important than drawing upon friends and co-workers is to draw upon yourself. Focus on your strengths in your moments of weakness. Nothing promotes success and well-being like success and well-being. Search out those activities at which you have a special sense of competence. Whether these activities are playing the violin, climbing mountains, or playing cards is not important. What counts is that you engage in some form of activity which shows that you are not as useless and worthless as the negative side of yourself makes out. If you have an intense interest in stamp collecting, sports, or *any* hobby, make use of it in times of stress. Such interests can go far towards giving you a feeling of competence and continuity which can help you through difficult times.

Above all, you must draw upon your inner resources in an attempt to find self-discipline. Self-discipline is probably the greatest attribute for overcoming mental stress on your own. If you can force yourself to go through the motions, even when feeling rotten, and stick to a normal pattern of activity you have a better chance of overcoming difficult periods. This is particularly true with regard to maintaining normal eating, sleeping, work, exercise, and leisure-time activities. If you can find the discipline to force yourself to perform your normal activities even when you don't feel up to it, you are more likely to pull yourself out of depressions and other mental crises than if you give in to them, and physically as well as mentally withdraw from your normal everyday world.

Once you have exhausted the personal resources, or if your particular mental problems seem immune to self-intervention, you should consider casting a broader net in your search for help. A good place to start would be non-medical resources — the counselling services of churches, schools, and private associations such as the Y.M.C.A., community centres, or the crises centres which are maintained in many cities. In Great Britain and a growing number of other parts of the world the SAMARITANS are in your 'phone book and are ready to help quell any kind of crisis (not only suicidal) in the realm of mental pain — *24 hours per day*. Keep ringing, should the number be engaged at first, until you get through. Volunteers in these organizations may not be able to help you if you have severe mental illness, but they are experienced and concerned and will be able to direct you to further avenues of professional help should you need them. In most cases the problem is not severe, and they will be able to provide some immediate relief as well.

If on consultation with any of these counsellors it becomes apparent that you need more intensive professional help, there are many options available to you. Most family doctors, although sometimes needing a determined push, *will* arrange for you to see an expert. Sometimes a voluntary counsellor can give you suitable names of known good men or women to suggest to your doctor and can lend his weight to making him arrange this for you.

For those with greater economic resources, private practice is the best source of help. Bureaucratic delays are eliminated. In private practice there is greater freedom of choice concerning the type of therapy and the personality of the practitioner. Private practice is usually more convenient to arrange and more private as you attend the doctor's home or private clinic rather than a general hospital.

Within the realm of professional treatment there is a wide range of different therapeutic philosophies and practices. Some of these will be discussed more fully in the section on treatment. Added to these are groups participating in transcendental meditation, yoga, Japanese body control therapy, dance therapy, and other therapeutic schemes and ideologies which have achieved varying degrees of success and acceptance around the world.

Any of these forms of therapy may help you. Which one is right for you depends on a large number of factors. Certainly not all are available in all places. The fact that there are so many different forms of therapy is an indication that there is no one single best solution to everyone's mental problems. Problems vary as much as personalities and the appropriate therapeutic treatment depends on a combination of the particular stresses in your life and your basic values and personality.

Studies have shown that the most important preconditions for successful therapy are belief in the particular type of therapy undertaken and confidence and trust in the therapeutic practitioner. If you are to engage in successful therapy, you must believe that you are participating in a worthwhile activity and that your sacrifices of time and money will be repaid by the attainment of improved mental health.

6

HOW TO HELP SOMEONE GET HELP

One of the most difficult tasks confronting friends and relatives of persons suffering from mental stress is how to get them to seek professional help for their problems. In our society to admit that you have mental problems takes extreme courage. Despite so-called advances and increased sophistication in the mental health field and wider presentations of mental health problems in the popular media, there is still an enormous stigma attached to those who are labled (libelled would be the more appropriate word) mentally ill, neurotic, or "crazy". This stigma remains long after the symptoms of mental illness have disappeared.

It is almost as if mental illness were viewed as a direct punishment from God, a formal state of disgrace or sin. To tell someone that he is neurotic and in need of professional help can't escape the negative consequences of this popular misconception. In most cases it is inevitable that advice to seek professional help will be misinterpreted by the potential patient to mean that he is either intrinsically weak or defective or that he must *permanently* abdicate his responsibilities and self-determination to others. That this is *not* the case should be made clear to anyone who may be in need of professional intervention.

In a society such as ours which values the independent, autonomous individual, to admit to the possibility of even temporary disability is a great burden, particularly for someone who is already suffering from mental stress. The very act of trying to get a relative to seek relief from mental stress may actually produce greater stress. It is no wonder that most people are reluctant to offer advice and that even more prefer not to listen when it's offered.

There is a way out of this bind. It requires tact and a simple basic understanding of the nature of mental problems. Mental problems are not allotted by the devil. They occur naturally as a result of the stresses of modern life and the conflicts in daily living which all human beings must experience from infancy until death, as the price for living in a large complex civilization. With the exception of relatively few major mental illnesses, most neuroses (and they form the vast majority of mental problems) are *not* congenital (we are not born with them). Rather, they are the result of the entire range of experiences of each individual, in which his biological constitution may play an entirely insignificant role. Despite claims to the contrary in some quarters, neuroses are *not* necessarily a sign of inadequate family upbringing or defects in those who raised you. Mental problems, by their very nature, are never produced by any single cause but by a complex interaction between a variety of factors which may include everything from biological constitution, family upbringing, the state of the economy, chance, the weather, and current social movements such as women's liberation or the civil rights movement.

We are going into this rather detailed explanation of where and why mental problems arise because only in this way can the stigma resulting from admitting to neurotic conditions be removed. There is no such person as a neurotic or psychotic in the sense in which it is understood and used as a label by the general public or by many psychiatrists and doctors as well.

There are people with problems and nothing more.

Particularly in the case of minor mental problems such as neurosis, there is a fine line which divides normal anxiety and unhappiness from neurotic suffering and unhappiness; and this line can only be drawn subjectively, not objectively or scientifically in the true sense of objectivity or science as understood by most laymen.

This is not to deny that people suffer from serious mental problems, nor to suggest that it is not a good idea for many such people to seek, and benefit from, professional help. What this view does imply, however, is that what needs to be treated are a person's problems and only a person's problems; not the core of his being nor his innermost private self. People who suffer from neuroses and other mental problems are not defective or inferior to those who don't. Remove the stresses which are causing their problems and the problems will subside. Society defines normal and abnormal behaviour and, but for a different definition (and in terms of normalcy all definitions are arbitrary to a greater of lesser extent), those considered sick would be considered healthy and those healthy, sick.

With all this by way of introduction, the question still remains – how do you help someone get help? First, you must embed this notion that your friend or relative is not really "sick" but suffering from stresses and mental troubles. Next, approach your friend honestly and directly. Tell him that he has not been acting himself of late. Explain how you have noticed loss of humour, tenseness, or whatever other symptoms this book has helped you uncover and understand. Be as specific as possible. Cite as many concrete symptoms or danger signals as you can.

The important factors in helping someone to get help are: (1) show the other person that you are concerned about his problems, while at the same time demonstrating your respect and admiration for him as a person. Make him feel what you know is true – that somehow, some particular stresses or problems in his life are preventing his better qualities from coming to the fore and interfering with his "normal" strong likeable personality. (2) If possible, offer an immediate and *concrete* suggestion as to where to go and what to do. Even if this concrete suggestion is no more than the name of a psychologist or social worker at a public clinic, offer it. There is a tremendous difference between telling someone to call a particular number and ask for a specific name and merely telling someone to call a doctor or see a "shrink". The naming of the doctor or social worker makes your friend's a specific human case, rather than a general dehumanized problem. (3) It takes courage to see a psychiatrist or psychologist for the first time. If possible accompany your friend right to the therapist's door and stay with your friend until the therapist can see him. Hold your friend's hand (literally if he wants or needs you to) and talk to him. If left alone, he might, at the last moment, walk out, making it even harder to get him to see someone than it was originally. Remind him that he is not "sick", that he is not seeing a therapist because he is "weak". Let him know that your high regard for him is not diminished by your realization that he is undergoing mental stresses and could use some help. In this way you break down the false distinction between "sick" and "healthy" personalities and make it easier for your friend to accept his mental problems and seek professional guidance.

7

PHILOSOPHY
OF MENTAL HEALTH

VIEWING MENTAL ILLNESS AS NORMAL ILLNESS

Mental illness is illness. It is not abnormal. It is not pathological (due to inherent weakness or disease). It is not a sign of personal condemnation by God. It is not a punishment for past sins. It is not a demonstration of family or personal unworthiness. It is an illness, which like any other illness, will occur under certain conditions and under others, won't.

Two people may both be exposed to a similar germ; one will get pneumonia or a virus attack and the other won't. The same holds true for neuroses and many other mental illnesses. However, as with physical diseases, there are certain conditions under which everyone will become ill if not given medicine or if not treated in some way. The very fact that we often talk of how someone is driving us crazy is proof that there are certain ways of treating people that almost inevitably produce mental illness. Similarly there seem to be biological predispositions for certain diseases. Nonetheless, even a predisposition requires that certain environmental factors be present for the disease to emerge.

It may be that A, with a predisposition for depression, would not develop a neurosis if he were born into family X but would if born into family Z. Likewise, B may have a predisposition for a different mental illness that would not present itself if he were born into family

Z but would if born into family X. This is a highly simplified and superficial example of what really produces mental illness, but the basic principle illustrated is true. Neither family Z nor family X is the "healthier" family. Either, both, or neither may produce a child with mental problems. The illnesses of the children are not categorically the family's fault (although there are cases where parents do a terrible job of raising children and where it is almost inevitable that mental problems arise; however, these cases are much more rare than either families or patients believe). There are so many outside factors, over which parents and families have little or no control, which contribute to the mental health of their offspring that it is futile to place the blame for a child's mental problems chiefly on the family or parents.

The truth is that we are living in a society which, at least in terms of mental health, does not provide a very healthy environment. The rapid changes, the leisure time, the luxuries, and the overwhelming choice of lifestyles, philosophies, and consumer products creates stresses and conflicts to a degree which seldom existed in the past. This is the price of "progress" but it is not our intention to condemn the great material advances of the twentieth century. It should merely be pointed out that such advances require a price or a sacrifice of something, as do all changes and acquisitions. In this case, increased freedom and prosperity seem to have been purchased with the sacrifice of certain securities and the tranquility of former times. As the preconditions for good physical health improve, the preconditions for good mental health seem to deteriorate. This is a fact which planners and civil servants might seek to change, but with which, at least for the time being, we must live and whose reality we must accept.

MOST PEOPLE CATCH COLDS

Most people at least occasionally catch colds. When they do they don't blame themselves or accuse those they are nearest to of having engineered the conditions of their cold. Depending on the cold's severity they either live with it at a diminished capacity until it passes, or stay in bed and rest until they feel better. There is no stigma attached to their being sick. Friends sympathize with their bad luck and give their support and sympathy.

Why can't this be the case with mental illnesses as well? Given the fact that there are probably more mental "germs" (stresses, tensions, conflicts, double bind situations — when you are deliberately (or unwittingly) placed in a position by someone else where whatever you do or say is "wrong" or "evil", etc.) floating around than cold germs, why are people ashamed to admit that they have mental problems? There is no specific label for someone with a cold, whereas to call someone neurotic, manic depressive, schizophrenic, or psychotic removes them from the circle of humanity to some nether world of abnormality or worse.

The truth is that people develop mental problems in a fashion not dissimilar to the way in which people develop physical illnesses. If you go outdoors on a rainy day and walk unprotected for a long period of time in wind and rain you are likely to fall ill. The same is true for mental illness. We are constantly exposing ourselves to mental stresses and it is inevitable that these stresses will produce problems. The only abnormal thing about the process is that we try to pretend it doesn't exist and shun, for as long as possible, the need to take care of our mental health. A cold infection or virus left untreated may develop into a case of pneumonia and even result in death. Untreated mental stresses will create neuroses and these, in turn, will become more severe if left unattended.

Only by bringing mental problems out into the open and attempting to deal with them in some concrete and positive form is there any hope for reducing mental anguish. If mental problems were treated as if they were physical problems (without losing sight of the significant and important differences) and the stigma of being mentally ill removed, much of the burden and suffering generated by mental problems would also disappear.

THE CONSTRUCTIVE POTENTIAL OF ILLNESS FOR STRENGTHENING THE INDIVIDUAL

One way in which mental illnesses could begin to lose their social stigma would be by a clearer understanding of what neuroses mean and the potential of someone, once he has worked through his mental problems, to be more creative, productive, compassionate, and just plain wiser than he would have been otherwise.

There is a fine line between creativity, a healthy imagination, and a crippling neurosis or psychosis (an unrealistic or fantastic way of viewing the universe which has negative consequences for the self or others). A little bit of neurosis may be useful to an artist or other creative person. If a patient can free himself from the debilitating effects of a neurosis while at the same time gaining an understanding of how and why his neurosis developed, he will unquestionably have a better sense of himself and understanding of human and mental dynamics than he would have had, had he not experienced mental problems.

8

WHAT CAUSES
MENTAL ILLNESS?

The answer to this question is potentially anything and never only one thing. Biology, family upbringing, interpersonal relationships, the society you live in, television, consumer capitalism, socialism, traumatic experiences — almost anything can contribute to the development of mental illness. Anything that creates stress and anxiety has the potential to produce mental illness. Because concepts such as stress and anxiety are vague and ultimately subjective evaluations, it is difficult to talk meaningfully of general causes of mental illness.

Nonetheless, recent studies have shown that there are certain periods in life and certain events which are highly associated with the outbreak of mental illnesses. These periods are generally known as transition states. Examples of these states are discussed below. If you are going through a transition state you can expect to be under more than normal stress and you should be on the lookout for symptoms responding to stage two — Emergency Regulatory Behaviour and stage three — Neurotic Coping Behaviour as described in this book. Likewise, if friends or relatives are going through transition states you should be particularly sensitive to the possible mental problems they may be encountering.

NINE TRANSITION STATES ASSOCIATED
WITH HIGHER RATES OF MENTAL ILLNESS

1. *New job, new school, new house.*
   All firsts are potentially destructive. No matter how positive or desired the change is there is always a high

degree of anxiety associated with first steps. Will the new job work out? Will co-workers accept me? Will I make new friends at school? Will my teachers like me? Will I be able to do the work? Will the children adjust to the new house? Will they make new friends? Will I? Such doubts can't fail to materialize and at times seem to be realized as well. At the same time, old friends and comfortable patterns of behaviour have had to be given up adding to potential (though by definition transitional) disorientation and demoralization of your inner mental world. Once the newness wears off and new friends are actually made and new adjustments made, the transition is over and the fears and anxieties subside.

2. *Gain or loss of a love partner.*

The gain is almost always a removal of more stress than it creates but not necessarily so. Added to the problems of newness as discussed in (1) above, there are two other disruptive factors. First is the reaction of those to whom you are currently close, including family. A new love partner is bound to affect your intimate friends and family. There may be personality clashes, disapproval, or just a required rearrangement of fundamental habits and activites. Second is the fear of loss which accompanies all new acquisitions and gains. This fear is not necessarily rational, but there is no denying that it exists and is the cause of much mental stress. Jealousy, possessiveness, and obsessive devotion are all possible manifestations of this fear of loss of a new love partner even during the first weeks of togetherness. Such fears are real and must be dealt with from the beginning of each new relationship.

The loss of someone truly loved is an extreme hazard for mental health. In the case of couples who have lived together for years there is the additional trauma of trying to rebuild an entire life with new sets of friends, new activities, and new roles as a single person. Such changes are difficult to handle at any time in one's life and with added grief and mourning become even more stressful and potentially destructive of one's mental balance and adaptability to everyday stresses.

3. *Physical illness.*

Physical illnesses, especially when protracted or debilitating, are likely to lead to mental illnesses as well. Even minor colds produce states of irritability and depression. Major illnesses often call for the abandonment of entire work, play, or love activities and an essential readjustment to all phases of life on the part of the patient. Particularly in modern society, which puts a premium on independence and individual autonomy, it is difficult to accept a dependent and passive role.

4. *Parenthood*

Any problems a marriage may have had are likely to reappear with the birth of offspring. If value conflicts or misunderstandings about the goals of the marriage have not been worked through, they may create stresses at this time.

5. *Unemployment*

Unemployment is difficult to accept. It creates financial problems, lowers a worker's self-esteem, creates much leisure time most of which is filled with worrying about finding a new job or hoping for the current lay-off to end, and generally causes havoc in one's life. It is common for the unemployed to feel useless and depressed. Their sense of purpose is gone and the major constant about which their life was organized and regulated — their work — is also gone. Exercise, sleeping, and eating patterns are often disturbed by unemployment, leading to both physical and mental problems. It is a period of anxiety for the worker's family as well, in which consumption patterns and customary "luxuries" will have to be reduced or discontinued. The standard of living which was taken for granted before losing one's job can no longer be maintained and countless adjustments, small and large, must be made.

6. *Adolescence.*

In adolescence appears the often cited "identity crisis" as the young person questions who he is and who he is to become. In adolescence each decision appears to be momentous, the key to the youth's entire future. Often, as with career decisions, this comes close to being the case. In such situations stress and tension is inevitable if there are even minor doubts about the decisions being taken. (As Margaret Mead's work *Coming of Age in Samoa* has shown, adolescence is not a stressful period for youth in other lands where these pressures and decisions are absent.)

7. *Menopause.*

For women, menopause is a particularly difficult transition from procreativity to sterility. They must adjust to a different self-image as well as contend with major biological changes within their body, which may affect mental stability as well.

8. *Death.*

The deaths of friends, lovers, parents, and family members are difficult moments in which to maintain mental adaptability. All human cultures have evolved elaborate rituals to ease the pain and mental anguish for those who survive the death of intimates. Death is doubly traumatic. First, it brings into play all the disturbing factors discussed in (2) above associated with the loss of a love partner. New patterns of living must follow the loss of major persons in your life and new adjustments and identifications of self must also be made. Daily life won't be the same after the loss of a parent or close friend and you know it.

Death in and of itself is probably the most disturbing fact of life. When close friends or family die something in us dies as well — memories, images, feelings, experiences shared. Death questions our most fundamental assumptions about ourselves and the meaning of our actions and existence as individuals.

9. *Old age.*

Old age is a uniquely difficult period of life. It is a transitional state in the sense that men and women must adapt to ever-decreasing mental and physical energies and learn to accept passive roles and dependence in the place of former active leadership roles in family and at work. Most difficult of all, old people must accept themselves for the life they have lived, knowing that they cannot relive differently that which is past, or hope for some future changes to justify past mistakes. They must accept their approaching death and resolve to live despite the loss of friends and the disappearance of most of that which gave their lives meaning and fulfilment in their youth and middle age.

In addition, as senility takes effect, brain cells die and may create a variety of severe mental illnesses, ranging from delusion to dementia (structural or organic deterioration of intellectual faculties with resulting emotional disturbance) and other forms of gross confusion. Deafness, blindness, and other illnesses requiring or resulting in social isolation and confinement produce conditions ripe for the outbreak of paranoia, insecurity, anxiety, and other stresses which in turn may lead to severe mental disorders.

9

TREATMENT

Informal treatment can be anything from joining a club, taking a vacation, having a discussion with your wife, or going out to dinner and a film. Such informal treatments are not going to make any major mental illness disappear. They might, however, enable you to weather emotional crises with less trauma and serve as preventitives against greater mental stress in the future. Given that the majority of minor mental problems are the result of transitional periods and adjustment periods in your life, such informal treatments can go far towards lessening the effects of a self-correcting mental problem.

Informal treatment lifestyles include participation in activities which are intended to improve your overall physical and mental health and which have specific philosophies or ideologies about how one ought to live. Examples are transcendental meditation, yoga practitioners, varieties of Eastern religions, communes, encounter groups, women's groups, etc. These treatment lifestyles demand a commitment to a particular set of values and require at least a partial restructuring of values and lifestyle. Vegetarianism, nudism, and even anarchism could be viewed in this manner; not because they are intended as therapeutic institutions, but because any total philosophy or demanding commitment cannot fail to have a significant effect (postive or negative) upon mental health.

Formal treatment of mental health problems includes all forms of therapy, medical or otherwise, which exist solely for the alleviation of mental problems. This includes all forms of analysis, both individual and group, behavioural therapies, and folk therapies such as spiritualism, astrology, fortune telling, etc.

THERAPY – WHAT IT IS AND ISN'T

Therapy is any treatment which is directed towards strengthening the patient's tolerance and control over his mental problems. Each therapeutic intervention should define specific treatment goals, to be agreed upon mutually by patient and practitioner. These goals may be vague as in psychoanalysis – to increase insight and understanding or to live a "fuller life" by raising self-esteem – or specific as in behavioural therapies – the avoidance or control of specific emotions or reactions, such as anger, stuttering, or sexual malfunction. Ideally, patient and therapist should reach an informal contract specifying expectations and commitments. Even in psychoanalysis totally open-ended arrangements are not in the best interest of either patient or doctor. Will drugs be used? Can therapy be broken off at any time? What will the cost be? All these questions should be dealt with *before* any form of therapy is begun.

All therapies have limited capabilities. No therapy should be expected to eliminate all sources of mental stress. Such an expectation is unrealistic and self-defeating. There are no miracles in therapy, no magic bullets or pills. No therapist has the secret of living a painless, satisfying, happy, complete life. If you go to therapy seeking such impossible results you will surely be disappointed. At best, therapy is both a supportive and strengthening activity which leaves you stronger and more capable of carrying on a satisfying life after therapy has been completed. At worst, therapy can be a rip-off of time and money and an imposition on your inner values, bringing only temporary or no relief to your emotional problems.

Therapy should not become a way of life, nor should it be used to avoid the real pains and conflicts which make up the process of living and changing. If this is the goal there are various ways of achieving it, from political commitments to success in business to satisfaction in artistic, musical, or other creative performance. Engage in them but not under the guise of formal therapy, for in that case your life will be but a mirror of someone else's definition of the world and not your own.

By definition therapy is a time-limited, temporary intervention. It should not be viewed as a way of avoiding or suspending any problems of living. In the final analysis any therapy can only succeed to the extent that you are willing to struggle and overcome specific realities of your life or your mental experiences. A therapist can help, but he can't do the job for you. You can overcome a problem only by working at it and not avoiding it. If you are unwilling to work at your problems there is little a therapist can do for you.

This is less true for behavioural therapy and certain folk therapies in which the patient is expected to remain totally passive. Even with these therapies, however, the patient must, as a minimum, have a desire to improve or to "get well". This type of therapy is basically the giving of aid, comfort, and support to a patient to alleviate external stresses and crises. Supportive therapies are generally short-term and are intended for self-terminating problems such as minor depression or temporary confusion.

THERAPY VIEWED CROSS-CULTURALLY OR A COMPARATIVE VIEW OF THERAPY

In other cultures therapies have evolved which emphasize group support and not individual change. There are countless rites and practices recorded for South and North American Indians, African tribes, and Asian peoples, which treat both mental and physical diseases by reintegrating the individual with his family and tribe. In a sense, most Western religious faith healers operate this way as well. Those who are ill are asked to dedicate themselves to God and through prayers and the attention of fellow believers they will be cured by God (note the so-called "miracle" cures at Lourdes in France).

What evidence there is suggests that such therapies for certain illnesses are nearly as successful as the formal medical therapies practiced by modern psychiatrists. The only hitch is that these therapies will only work for people who believe in them. You must have faith in God, the gods, ancestors, spirits, drugs, or other powers invoked for the rite to heal. This does not mean that modern therapies are merely modernized versions of ancient superstitions. Anthropological evidence suggests that such rites incorporated many scientifically valid principles in their operation, which modern therapies would do well to emulate. Nonetheless, given the vast complexity and secularization of the modern world, it is unrealistic to attempt to return to past forms of treatment whose efficacy came from symbols whose meaning, let alone power, has long since faded for the majority of twentieth-century people.

THE INDIVIDUAL AND SOCIETY

In any discussion of treatment, mention must be made of the relationship that exists between the individual and the society in which he lives. Bluntly, this relationship is one of inherent conflict.

Animals do not suffer from depression and other mental diseases, except in response to immediate physical deprivation. For man, living in a complex society in which all men are to a large extent interdependent, the price which must be paid for the successful maintenance of the society as a whole is the repression of basic individual desires. This conflict between individual desires and the desires of the group is at the base of much mental stress and mental illness.

Many therapies and therapists emphasize the need of

the individual to conform to the demands of society. For them, successful adjustment to society is the goal of therapy. This works fine when the patient and therapist are in agreement about what constitutes "successful adjustment" but the problem of all analytical therapies is precisely this: How are the best interests of the patient going to be defined and what values and world-view will the therapy support? When basic values between therapist and patient are in serious conflict, the therapy is doomed to rocky, unproductive struggles.

In Soviet Russia some therapies have become nothing more than tools for forcing conformity to a particular set of values. The degree to which this is true of any particular therapeutic encounter in our own country depends upon the integrity and openness of the therapist and the therapist-patient relationship which is established. In all therapeutic encounters there is some disguised societal coercion. The significance of this coercion can be lessened by recognition and discussion of the problem by therapist and patient.

NO-FAULT ILLNESS

Much suffering would be avoided if the notion that no one is to blame for the occurrence of mental illness could be accepted. Mental illness is not a sign of individual debility. It is not the fault of parents, teachers, siblings, neighbours, lovers, or friends. Or better, all of society is to blame and all of society is blameless. Man is a social animal. His social environment is part of his natural environment, as necessary for his survival as air or water. An individual does not choose to be born into a particular society. His birth is a natural event and the conflicts that develop between the individual and his social world also occur in a random fashion. In this sense, mental illness, which is caused by a combination of individual, social, and natural events, is an impersonal event as blameless and uncontrived as cancer or other physical diseases.

As men we can increase the likelihood of illnesses occurring by polluting the world and creating unhealthy living conditions or we can diminish that likelihood by dedicating ourselves to improving the total social and natural environment in which we live. To do so is in the interest of most men and is the central goal of nations and civilizations. That we fail is no particular person's or group's fault. We fail because we are men and as men we are imperfect, weak, frightened creatures most of the time, rising above these weaknesses only through great determination and a good deal of helpful chance.

We do not fail because we are evil or because it is our will to create mental illness and see our children and fellow men suffer. To put the blame for mental illness on particular men is to blame all men for being men, to see the state of man as something evil, and to indulge in the masochism of glorified self-hate. It is nobody's fault, not even the creator's, that we are as we are. And it is no one's fault *per se* that we create the conditions under which mental illness thrives.

This is little solace to those suffering the agony of mental torment. It removes the one last positive pleasure of the neurotic of at least being able to curse himself or someone else for his misery, to be able to blame someone for his pain; and yet, only when a man arrives at the realization that neither he, nor his parents, nor those he may have hated or loved are truly responsible for his suffering can he begin to overcome it. This is not to imply that the suffering of mental illness is in the order of things as they are and must be tolerated – not at all. That would deny the purpose of this workbook on mental illness. What *is* implied, however, is a view which will free the anguished and tormented man suffering from mental illness from the self-destructive and ultimately imprisoning and false view of himself and his society which attempts to punish in the past rather than liberate in the future.

10

SELF-CURE PROGRAMME
By M.M.

INTRODUCTION BY WILLIAM GLADSTONE

This chapter on self-cure and parapsychologic cure is included as examples of directions towards which mental health cure should move. There are too many problems in today's world for psychiatrists to treat adequately (and more important, to provide the kind of preventative care suggested in this book) the millions of people involved with mental problems (virtually every human being). In the United States, there is one psychiatrist for every 9,000 Americans, in Great Britain, even fewer.

It is in the hope of promoting self-treatment and parapsychologic treatment that TEST YOUR OWN MENTAL HEALTH has been written. Parapsychologic treatment is treatment by someone who knows something about psychology and is sensitive to human problems without being a "professional". The author who contributed this chapter is such a man. He is a helper, not an expert.

As an anthropologist I am both an expert and a helper. As an expert I would caution readers that the following modes of self-cure will not work for everyone. I must also add that in many cases psychiatrists ARE *necessary* and that there are individuals whose mental conditions deteriorate to the point that they become dangerous to themselves and or to others. These latter people should be dealt with through our legal system rather than mainly through our mental health system as is sometimes the case. Psychological help may be essential as well but mental problems should be no excuse for cruel or criminal actions. Fortunately, the majority of sufferers from mental problems are not dangerous but merely confused and unhappy. It is for these people that the kind of self-treatment described could most easily be used.

No therapy can be successful unless the patient *wants* to participate and change. Concerned friends and family can help as long as they offer *sincere* concern and love and not "expertise". It is difficult to differentiate between altruism and *self-interested* meddling. Great caution must be exercised in offering "advice". Friendship, interest, an attentive ear, and concern are appreciated by everyone, whether suffering from mental problems or not. This kind of genuine attention can motivate an individual to seek out further help in striving for successful self-cure.   W.G.

IS SELF CURE POSSIBLE?

Mental disorder should be curable: what follows explains why. Mental illness is often an exaggerated description because having a temporarily troubled mind is hardly abnormal. The line is only crossed into illness when putting such troubles behind you with reasonable ease becomes impossible. The technique for doing this may be ingrained and natural or may need to be *learned* and continuously improved. It is no shame if luck, upbringing and environment did not equip you with methods which work for you but there is nothing to prevent anyone from learning what to do, from whatever time in life illness may strike.

CASE REPORT: MRS. X

A 55 year old woman was diagnosed incurable by two internationally renowned psychiatric specialist doctors and two general physicians; one of whom was her own general practitioner. All four recommended this lady be institutionalized and they predicted the patient would never recover. The senior specialist told the family the sufferer would enter the sick, dream-world of the insane.

Here's why! The woman, who we will call Mrs. X, was no longer open to reason and anyone who tried to help her was met by Mrs. X sitting motionless, blocking each ear with a finger. To talk to her, at this advanced stage of her illness, was to waste breath. The diagnosis was paranoia.

Diagnosis and judgment. It is good news for the mentally ill that even such distinguished doctors can be wrong. They submitted, with all the authority their positions provided, their "final" adverse opinions. Each one, however, failed to address himself even to the first practical step towards cure. No reassurance was given to patient or family about the possible passing nature of such ills; just as a fit of bad temper normally fades, so bouts of trouble in the mind can subside. Indeed the reverse, the "permanence" of the condition was stressed!

Among several symptoms, the patient had come to believe her next door neighbour, an American Church leader, was in love with her. This good man and Mrs. X had twice attended a Church convention as representatives. The clergyman had given no cause to encourage the patient to imagine he was in love.

With passing years, Mrs. X had allowed herself to read more into the clergyman's smile than the parson had intended. She had fantasized that there was more behind the friendship than friendship. A single tiny gift in return for some help Mrs. X had given, became a love token in her thoughts.

Thus, through illogical emotional thinking, we see the seeds of madness being sown. In fertile soil such seeds grow big.

Eighteen months later, when her friend's wife died, Mrs. X saw God's hand at work. About the same time, by coincidence, Mrs. X's husband became gravely ill. Yes, here was another "message" from on high.

Mrs. X felt the Almighty was encouraging her. She realized her clergyman was now free to marry. By now the lady dreamed she was to be the chosen vehicle to marry him and to give birth to a second Christ; it was hardly surprising that she left her husband, who had taken ill, to die instead of tending him. In her imagination it would have been evil to interfere with, what to her, had become God's will.

Notice how run-away false thinking affects the mind.

The day before Mrs. X was to go into care, a friend persuaded the doctors and her three adult children to allow him to try some unorthodox therapy in the hope of saving the patient from the Hell on earth, or living death, we call madness. In their sane moments the so-called insane suffer indescribably. The risk of allowing such uncontrolled notions to start, let alone permitting them to flourish, is a danger which should be more widely known. Why is it our teachers so rarely teach us the useful things?

RETURN TO SANITY

What seemed impossible was simple. This experienced man spoke to the patient but each time the talks touched her illness, the ear-blocking was resumed and Mrs. X refused all advice.

The friend, however, was resourceful. He locked the door and shouted loudly so that the patient could not fail to hear.

He reiterated countless truths, for instance, how could Mrs. X at 55 give birth to a second Christ, how could a leading clergyman marry an already married woman (her husband had survived) and stressed the pain which remaining ill would inflict on her life and family. Over and over he released such healing truths to enter the patient's mind and no better psychological medicine exists.

These sessions continued for an hour daily for 18 days. On the last day, without warning, the patient left her friend's house and returned to her own home, *cured*. She immediately went back to her job and looked after her family as if she had not been ill.

This was 25 years ago.

Now over 80, Mrs. X remains fit and plays an active part in the community. Her children and grandchildren are proud of her and rightly. It was a great recovery. It is an example to all of us.

WHAT HAPPENED

Help was needed; it was given. At some point in the treatment the patient decided to accept the "how to think" medicine. That was the turning point, the rest followed.

Mrs. X spotted that blocking her ears TOTALLY was, as it always must be, silly.

The shouting broke through the *totality* of her barrier and she allowed herself a measure of receptiveness. This was despite considerable anger towards the shouter for "daring" to contest her views.

She learned the crucial truth that it was necessary to let what was being said to her, come in. Only in this way could she regain the chance to consider each idea and either accept or reject it, *using her own brain*.

Some of what was shouted is likely to have been off target. No matter. The method broke through with sufficient ideas to which she gave consideration, to provide the focus of her self cure. The message here is, *total* ear-blocking is madness.

Prick up your ears, instead! Consider the ideas only, untinged by annoyance with the person giving them or the particular way he or she may do it. After all no one is perfect, so why should someone trying to help be perfect at it?

The doctors described the cure as a miracle. Not so. It was a victory for commonsense over theory, applied with diligence, confidence and sufficient force. Mental patients who decide to examine sound advice and wish to get better, should recover fully.

SELF-CURE

The case described was grave. Most mental confusion, for that is what so much mental illness is, is easier to deal with and sufferers can frequently cure themselves.

We have seen how inaccurate thinking starts up; feeds on itself and becomes exaggerated. Such thinking is often obsessive as thoughts repeatedly whirl round in the heated brain. The person may turn in to himself or herself because of fears and worry. Such inward looking is bad for mental health; a dangerous state may be reached where remaining in misery is preferred to reaching the happiness in which normal people live.

One fear which breeds this nonsensical and apparently apathetic condition is that coping with normal life will be impossible. The sufferer foresees only failure after failure if he or she were to re-enter everyday life. The fact that such "failures" are only in the mind is overlooked. The sufferer is reacting, even preparing for these mental picture situations, to such an extent that when one of them *is* reached in real life, failure *is* likely. This is because the mind will be so preoccupied with its preconceived (and negative) notions of how events will turn out, that it will be unable to adapt to events as they *are*. (Thus the boy who places his girl upon a pedestal fails to notice her faults as well as her charms and fails to react to her real person while they are together).

THE VICIOUS MENTAL CIRCLE

When overheated the brain works in a vicious circle, a factor which seems to go against breaking out of the mess. Trying too hard to solve a problem, or overwhelmed by a succession of disasters, or attempting to resolve everything at once (even though you *know* nothing in life is achieved except step by step) overheats the brain: when overheated, confusion prevails: being confused prevents reaching conclusions: continued trying maintains the strained state and, round you go. Upset upon upset.

This vicious circle can grip a person till help arrives; it is hard for non-sufferers to understand that although the state can be reached in days, it may take months for a brain to cool off completely, ready to tackle the original worries. Partial cooling off usually occurs in hours, easing the pain, but repeated attempts to "get something done" top up the overheated state again. Thus a victim without access to the best advice may remain gripped for years. He may not cool off sufficiently to realize that some of the "problems" on his mind were not worth solving at all. He continues uselessly beating the air as he tries to "solve" everything.

Inability to cope is depressing, especially if combined with no hope of getting out of this quicksand of misery. The sufferer finds it hard to hope when, as is so often the case, there is no one near with the knowledge, ability and time to reassure him about what is happening and how his health *will* be restored. Often those nearest and dearest feel powerless and are almost equally at a loss with the patient to know where to turn. To a surprising extent mental breakdowns are "infectious".

Doctors have established that in depression minor changes in the brain chemistry occur. Suffice to say that these changes are enough to ensure that decision making becomes difficult. This effect is part of the confusion in the vicious circle.

WHAT MUST BE DONE?

The ill person and those guiding him or her must insist on relaxing totally. If possible the person should leave the home, office, etc., and get, temporarily, into new surroundings with new people. (Later, a permanent change may be desirable.) He or she should not even have to worry about making a shopping list, for example.

The need is to learn to relax. The patient must realize that *none* of the "problems" are to be thought about at all. Every time one of them returns to his mind he must say "NO! I cannot deal with this yet; my priority is to regain health, since I cannot function without it."

"Drop everything!" (as gunmen say), and calm down. Rest. No time limit can be set for this, even by the patient. He or she will soon enough become aware when they are ready to do a few bits and pieces again. A slow build up is then wise. Every case is different; some only need hours, some several weeks. Success is in the patient's own hands. If he goes meddling with his problems he will slow down his cure. In so far as he doesn't, speed will be at his side.

EARLY SIGNS OF MENTAL TROUBLE

In early mental trouble the person usually knows that he is thinking wrongly but such is his worry or depression, that he allows himself to accept the false thoughts. At this incubation stage the sick mind is easiest to restore to health.

Later, with repeated circular thinking truth becomes masked by inaccurate, often emotional, reasoning. In time, if allowed to go on, the sick person may begin to believe only his views are right, everyone else's wrong. He may even forget it is he who is ill.

To some extent such thinking comes from refusal to

accept advice or to believe what is true. To this degree, mind sickness may hide an act, put on as an escape from a potentially frightful experience the sufferer "fore-sees" but does not want to face. It may hide a cowardice in coming to terms with facts about an event which *has* happened. To get away from the whirl of such thinking *requires* discussion of the disaster or potential one, with a friend. It is the process of turning these thoughts into words, spoken to your friend that brings the ideas into focus and places upon them the test of reality.

Such acting can be superb; many who met Mrs. X while at the height of her illness had no idea she was unwell. Acting is NOT LIVING.

An illness is not the sufferer's fault. Blaming others or oneself is useless but the sick should realize while some of the cause of the illness may be physical, much of it usually arises, continues and expands in the mind. Unwise thinking has grown twelve feet tall and taken over. That's all. The upset person must get a hold of these facts and embed them deeply in his mind. Reality must replace pretence.

Physical causes such as toxins in the blood causing chronic poisoning and muzziness — leading to confused thinking and the vicious circle — can be ruled out once appropriate tests have been made by a good doctor. If a physical cause *is* discovered, so much the better, but restoration of good thinking will need to be part II of the cure. Centred in that thinking must be the realization that, just as after a bodily illness or operation, new health can surge back, so mental health is restored with the cure.

DETAILS OF SELF-TREATMENT

Some bodily causes are well-known, for instance, after a baby is born the mother may suffer depression, and who has not felt low following influenza? Such depression will be deepened if thinking is allowed to float around into nonsenses such as have been described. The good news is that such depressions usually ease quickly of their own accord. This is perhaps all the patient needs to be reassured. Millions have recovered with time and returning health.

In such instances temporary use of drugs, or tonics, monitored by a doctor who understands the mechanisms by which this sort of drug can help, may speed recovery. (If the doctor cannot explain to you what the drug is meant to be doing the chances are he doesn't know enough about it to be prescribing the right drug in the right dose for you.) Their main object is usually to slow down mental activity, reducing that urgency to get somewhere on something, and to improve relaxation. With their help clear thinking becomes possible again as the brain relaxes.

But no drugs can cure incorrect thinking. Sometimes when a psychiatrist makes prolonged use of drugs I'm afraid it is done to cover up his ignorance of how to treat the patient. It is the power of mind over matter, as the saying has it, which is the supreme magic in recovery. Correct lines of thinking management are essential.

Sensitive good people frequently suffer most. Some insensitive remark such as "all your life you have been a selfish girl, I don't know how your husband puts up with you" can cause lasting havoc. Healthy people who know themselves, laugh off such remarks. It must be stressed, non-acceptance of nasty comments removes all the sting. Because someone says something does not make it true, whoever says it. What you don't accept does you no harm.

The start up of mental troubles are infinitely variable. Some may be attached to the past. Most people carry in their minds some feelings of guilt, fears of various kinds which are inbred from our backgrounds. A mother dies and one of her children (possibly the nicest of them) begins to feel she did not treat her mother well. Men or women get guilt-ridden over former sex behaviour or failures or feel they have been unkind to a loved one and suffer mental agonies. Had they but discussed this with their loved one they might have discovered that he or she felt no such hurt as was being imagined — and being allowed to depress the over-sensitive partner.

None of us is perfect but true or false, in such matters a stand must be made. A firm stand. The past cannot be undone; if one has made mistakes sometimes they can be compensated for, but beyond that, the past must be put behind you. Life is too short. Even shorter. Thinking should be directed to the future. As we forgive others, so, if we have done something against our conscience, we must forgive ourselves. No one can be happy living under a cloud of guilt.

SELF DIAGNOSIS

It's hard to know when one is becoming ill. The line between robust mental health and illness is fine but often in the beginning is a realization that certain unusual thoughts are flowing into our heads. Back they come, back and back again! Round and round they whirl in obsessional circles. Uncontrollably? Yes almost — even at the start of an illness. Later you learn how to fight back.

Judicious use of TEST YOUR OWN MENTAL HEALTH and other people may help us know something is wrong. Remarks like "Snap out of it," "What's biting you?" are part of everyday language but could indicate that something is going amiss. Pay attention and consider. That's what warning signals are for.

THE BATTLE OF AND FOR YOUR LIFE

Once you realize you are getting ill act now, not tomorrow. Say to yourself, "today I start and I shall not give up till victory".

We are not here dealing with mental conditions which arise entirely through a bodily breakdown. In some crippling instances, nothing but admiration beyond words is due to sufferers. Such breakdown it should be noted by those prone to jumping to conclusions, may be no less real for being *invisible* and perhaps yet undiagnosed, for example poisoning caused by partial liver failure. Physically broken-down people who achieve such miracles do so by using such positive life-restoring thinking as we describe here. They are an example to everyone. Human beings seem to be given grace, as those of us who have faced death realize, to bear all sorts of suffering.

Don't despise yourself because these damaging thoughts enter and re-enter and return yet again into your mind. This also happens to the mentally robust. Feel not ashamed, for mental sickness of one variety or another will affect us all if we live long enough. No one is so strong he can prevent harmful thoughts converging into his higher centres. They are part of life but when cured can be regarded as a nightmare which may well have helped us to better understand ourselves and the human condition. Was it not Solomon who asked to be granted wisdom above all else?

Mrs. X needed powerful outside help. Many people can cure themselves once they are shown how. Where the illness has not bitten as deeply as Mrs. X's here are good methods.

The first requirement is recognition of illness in yourself. This book has shown how comparative observations can prove when you need to restructure thinking. The second is a decision that you want to get better. With so many happy people outside proving that it is unnecessary to remain miserable, why go on doing it? The third is the knowledge that you are entering the battle not only of your life, but for it.

Compare your trouble to a decayed tooth. To restore it means that, not 88% but 100% of the decay must be dug out before it is repaired with sound material. So with an out of order mind. Every hurtful, negative, unhappy, disorder-creating notion must be met, examined, and appropriately altered, discarded, or replaced with good health-making thoughts.

THERE'S A LIMIT TO YOUR THINKING CAPACITY!

It follows because time does run out that as well as just thinking, you should organize what are your priority subjects for thought. Otherwise one may get bogged down desperately trying to think about everything at once, or doing the opposite and spending all the time thinking obsessively about one thing. Either error leads to chaos like an unmanaged football team in which no player is in the right place at the right time. Thus Mrs. X at the beginning of her breakdown did not appreciate the necessity of analysing her situation and discovering whether the true position was NOT, what in her imagination, she allowed herself to dream up.

She was so locked in to thinking about the details of the clergyman's love for her (the lovely details in her imagination) that the simple test of asking him directly if he had any such feelings was either overlooked or, far more likely, feared because it was bound to bring down the edifice of her creation. She did not give house room to the idea that the notion was silly and merely speculation in her mind.

We have explained why discussion is often crucial in sorting out such false thinking. Repose your confidence in someone you can trust to share a confidence. No need to shout all around about your troubles. This only courts gossip from surface thinking minds who (for their own gain, because they think spreading gossip makes *them* interesting and they have little of their own to talk about) would try to attach false shame to your difficulties.

NEW THINKING

One of the hardest things is to stop the rot increasing in our heads. New thinking along the lines described needs to chase away the old. Squeeze out the sick thinking and it will give up and die away as the disordered mind restores itself to normality.

When you notice you are being obsessed by one subject but perhaps can't decide whether it is worth all the worry, switch on to something else, especially something which makes you happy, like fishing, going to the movies, playing tennis or any hobby, or perhaps best, going out with an old friend. This mind switching plays an immense part in taking the heat out of the brain box and in the return to reality and joyous life. The mental switch dissipates what of old would have been called evil spirits. Change direction and let these "spirits" dance outside till *they* tire, not inside till they tire you! Avoid sitting around depressing yourself.

In mental illness the body often gets out of condition. It is vital to take daily exercise be it a good walk, jogging or sport. *Imperative*.

Once the tide of wrong thinking, so overwhelming to the sufferer, is turned back, recovery can be with you in days and it doesn't much matter how long you may have been ill, lacking only the right approach. There are few things in the world so wonderful as to see a cure happening. The patient in his or her nightmare state often sees odds of 100 to 1 against recovery and backs up this view by declaring that they "can't" be helped because no one "understands" them. The good news, known to those who can help, whether qualified by experience or training, is that the odds are the other way round, 100 to 1 *for* complete recovery.

Whether a person is fighting alone or being helped he can remain cheerful with hope from the moment he perceives that cure *is* around the corner, WITHIN HIS

GRASP, THE NEW STYLE GRASP, TO WHICH THIS BOOK IS POINTING THE RIGHT WAY.

People harass themselves about what may happen to them, are anxious about tomorrow's or next year's problems, or frustrate themselves trying to solve difficulties which defy resolution simply because facts are not at hand. You can't, for example, solve a problem which requires a look at your bank statement presently in your "In" tray at the office, while you lie awake in bed at 4 in the morning at home. Leave it alone till you reach the office, or bring the statement home next day! But don't thrash at the problem while the material facts are elsewhere.

No. Try to live out each moment, each day, each week as it arrives, achieve each thing you want to, be it so humble as buying an ice cream or so mighty as writing a poem, when *you* can manage it — and only if you can — till health returns. Most of the disasters we fear never materialize.

FEELING INFERIOR

But for this or that, perhaps unlucky happening, many anxiety conditions might never have arisen.

Shyness and inferiority feelings are at the root of numerous troubled minds. Hoards of theories are expressed as to how to get over them. The zealous devotees of one school of thought or another have produced whole new "languages" for the sheep to follow. Perhaps this all adds mystique for their brethren or is intended to suck in more adherents, as a weasel bewitches a rabbit. A look at them may do little harm but never accept ideas that do not make sense to you. Use your own brains.

The cure that lasts for life is to remove the inferiority — which in turn dispels the connected anxiety — or recognition that being inferior in a particular area of competence does not make you some kind of *complete* idiot! Nobody is expert at everything and everyone can beat me at something. No one else expects you to be a conglomerate genuis; why expect so yourself?

Few people would imagine, if they could not drive a racing car as well as the current world champion, that they were therefore inferior. Nor would they expect to excel at other *specialized* activities. Yet, when they come across a brilliant conversationalist or try to compare themselves with friends who achieve instant success with the opposite sex and things like that, these same people drop straight into the self made abyss of inferiority. Ridiculous really. Everybody can't be world champion. If another fellow is a conversational specialist but *you haven't* given the skill similar undivided attention, naturally you won't be as good at it.

It is easier to recognize that you do not need to become a great racing driver than to accept that maybe it is no use aspiring to the wit of a Winston Churchill, because we *all* want to be able to be interesting in company. Competitiveness in conversation is destructive anyway, as the effort of trying to go one better is exhausting and unnecessary.

If conversation is a problem, or anything else which it is reasonable to realize you cannot get along well without, than tackle it head on and conquer. Like the man who mumbled and could not speak well who practised on the seashore and so as to make it more difficult put pebbles in his mouth. He worked hard and in the end became the greatest public orator in the land.

Take practical steps. Obtain books on the art of interviewing and conversation, look out for and read articles on the subject; learn how. Work out your plan for victory and allow time for success to grow. Never insult or batter yourself inside should you prove to fail a little on the way, at some particular gathering. Just as you would not insult a friend, be friendly to yourself!

Try not to be unrealistically ambitious; over-ambition frequently makes people ill. It is fine to aim high but to aim above your potential or to expect to reach a goal within a time-scale which ignores the number of steps required on the way will cause mental exhaustion. Lower your sights to possible targets. Don't overload your plate; that's mad! Reconsider your ambitions. Are they your own or have you just been infected with them by well-meaning teachers, parents, friends etc? Choose the priority ones: discipline the rest to wait their turn. They may have to be displaced by better or different ones later anyway.

SEX WORRIES

Among younger people much anxiety stems from the widely held false view that one "must" have a boyfriend or a girlfriend in order to be happy. Later on the occasional ill mannered remark such as "aren't you married yet?" nurtures this festering belief.

There is no "must" to it. A wonderful partner is the bonus to which the happy person rightly aspires; each *adds* to the other's happiness but they were *not* part of it to begin with. If you are unhappy without one, you'll be just as unhappy with, unless that person can show you, as this book has tried to do, how to be happy inside.

Ask yourself how you are going to attract the *right* partner if you are allowing the lack of one to make you walk small? It's the mentally fit lovers who attach themselves to each other with true love. Attend to fitness first and walk tall.

IMPOTENCE AND FRIGIDITY

Impotence and frigidity are as common as colds. Psychological impotence, where men believe they are impotent, is a frightening anxiety, but unnecessary. It is

cured when the man realises and *accepts* that he is virile.
All that happened was he was paralysed by fear and the
largely involuntary reflex actions causing erection,
failed to operate. (In erection, the organ fills up with
blood). Short of some physical cause a person does not
ever become suddenly impotent. Impossible.

There is no logic to the complaint. The sufferer may
awaken with an erection. He still can't believe himself
virile, yet the evidence stands. It is wrong because, when
asleep, his fear left him and all was well. He finds this
hard to accept, but until he does he will have troubles.
Accept the truth and manhood is restored. One is dead
or alive, impotent or virile. No one is suddenly $\frac{1}{2}$ or .625
impotent!

Another common cause of mental worry in men is
premature orgasm, that is, the ejaculation occurs before
the couple are ready. Not long ago I heard of a
free-association analyst who told a patient this was due
to his fear of women and it was nature's way of showing
it. Was ever greater piffle spoken! Nature is a lot wiser
than we.

The causes of hasty orgasm are normally twofold. (a)
A vigorous young male will have plentiful seminal fluid
and have it in store after a few days' abstinence; thus his
first orgasm may be gorged with semen and then *no
willpower can prevent early ejaculation*; so the fellow
need not, as some do, imagine himself mentally weak-
willed. (b) Once a man gets this fear embedded in his
mind, he not unnaturally thinks, "Oh God, I must get
into the vagina before I come off!" Bad thinking.
Usually combined with the self damning question,
"what is my girl thinking of me?" If only he asked *her*
she might help him reach the solution. Cures are easier
with co-operation.

It's the attempt to enter quickly itself that is too much
and defeats control. The extra friction at just the wrong
moment brings on ejaculation.

Suggested remedies: reduce the time between inter-
courses so that excessive male fluid does not build up,

increase the time taken in love-play so that the man and especially the woman have become more lubricated, making entry easier. Don't rush to get in, putting on pressure is to ask for failure.

Here's why. Erection begins through anticipation and, or, stimulation, strengthening itself with the initial pleasures of touch and growing joyous feelings, which combine in a myriad of ways with the other senses. Depending on the level of excitement and the intensity of the other factors the point of orgasm, where semen urges to burst out, can be reached pretty quickly, even in seconds. Too much friction once the hyper-tense phase just preceding orgasm is reached will trigger ejaculation.

The secret is, as erection becomes firm, to allow extra time for it to become fully established before moving to the hypertense phase. Insert a delay. Or several. With practice the onset of the hypertense phase can be anticipated far enough ahead to hold back from getting into it and risking the premature pleasurable explosion you seek to defer.

Once erect, don't hurry, just enjoy each other with other love play keeping the erect penis clear of friction as much a you can till you are both ready. Stop and lie still if need be and breathe deeply, slowly while you simmer down. Then you can continue at will. Both give and receive love play enjoyment, just "nibbling" ear lobes or whatever. Murmur if the need be to each other, so that you will both know when you are both ready to fulfil the thrill of thrills, and can do so. The cure can take time but console yourself with the knowledge that, in the young, probably more than half of men have so suffered till cured.

I can hear someone saying, "Ah, the cure is more dangerous than the disease. Fancy recommending extra use of sex. This could cause real, permanent trouble."

More armchair nonsense. Look at wild animals — or tame ones — they get sex hungry as do humans. Do they all become impotent? Not likely! Nature takes care of us when we love. It would be awful if she did not. Any man who tries to over-do sex soon finds, (a) that he is satisfied and wants no more, and (b) even if he wanted more he couldn't get it because nature cries "enough for now". In a day or two desire and the ability to satisfy it, build up. Over frequency reduces pleasure.

Frigidity, etc. Although this *is* a worry for many women, it rarely causes *severe* mental trouble. The condition is normally curable and many other books exist which should be able to help, as can some doctors.

After the change of life some women run into physical problems and sometimes, usually minor, psychological ones. Again visit your doctor.

OLD AGE PROBLEMS

The difficulties of extreme age have been ably dealt with on page 143 but I would like to add a few thoughts.

Doctors using modern medicines can do much to make life happier for the aged but there is something one can do for oneself. Many folk who reach a milestone, maybe as young as the 60th birthday, but more likely older, drop into the habit of allowing themselves to become depressed by morning thoughts, such as "I'm 60 today", or "I'm over 75", and lie in bed dwelling on such a sad theme. Or the thoughts may relate to a lost partner such as, "John has gone now; life if not worth living for me". Or even a general thought like, "I haven't long left now."

Such wakening dreams should be fought against, for they can't prolong life and may help to shorten it, so dependent is bodily health on the attitude of mind and the quality of our thinking.

Better to greet each morning cheerfully. "It's raining today but I will get up now and visit that art gallery I've always wanted to." You are more likely to hit a healthy 90 if you aim at 100! Try not to let retirement, the loss of loved ones, or age mean dropping out of everything.

SUMMING UP

A large part of cure rests on faith and hope that a return to health is possible. Sometimes a helper, even a doctor, may not be able to explain to a person why an illness will be overcome; he just *knows* because he has seen similar recoveries. If you have a doubt, drop it and give the benefit of that doubt to faith. Faith has incredible mental healing power, like nothing else on earth.

As one fights the battle for mind health another useful trick is to notch up each victory, not on an imaginary spear as the Indian braves did but in your mind. Say to yourself, "I've won that round." Praise yourself too if you win a second round. If a friend in similar circumstances would deserve praise then *you* deserve it; allow yourself this honour; you're as good as the next man. The third round may be lost but fight on. Victory here, as so often elsewhere, usually comes to those who never despair, never yield or if they run away, it is only to reserve themselves, to return to win another day.

At some point during a breakdown a person may find he or she has learned more about the causes of the disorder, and consequently the cure for it, than the busy doctor who is treating him or her. In effect the once sick person can become their own "doctor." Fortunately this can and often does herald a permanent return to health, and it can soon be agreed with the doctor that treatment should cease.

Millions of sufferers have travelled the road before you. There is one man whose illness was, in several ways, harder to cure than Mrs. X's because it was more reasonable, and he found no-one able to guide him. Yet his troubled mind was restored to health in a few months, and he has been so happy he would not change one moment of his life. That was 44 years ago. So cures can be permanent.

11

SUPPLEMENTARY DIAGNOSTIC CHECKLISTS FOR REAPPRAISAL

Here is a second set of diagnostic checklists and in Chapter 12 is a second mental health visual Self-Evaluation chart. They are intended for use as a reappraisal of your original diagnosis or as a check against your original point score.

As indicated at the beginning of the book, it is a good idea to get at least two separate readings of your mental health, corresponding to different moods and circumstances. Alternatively, this supplementary chart can be used to measure if and how your mental health changes over time.

For calculation of point scores and interpretation, refer back to to the original diagnostic checklists as presented from page 89.

DIAGNOSTIC CHART   Characteristic 1: Tension

BEHAVIOUR AND SYMPTOMS

1. Tension has cause in the present or past.
2. Can do something that helps.

3. Clear-cut signs of tension (agitation, breathing, sweating).
4. Tension may or may not inhibit work.

5. Signs of tension with no apparent cause.
6. Tension inhibits work (most of the time).

7. Dependent on strong defences to make tension bearable.
8. Periods of nearly unbearable anxiety with no obvious cause.

9. Tension feels unbearable in absence of medication.
10. Tension only relieved by psychotic thinking (distortions, hallucinations, grossly inappropriate plans).

NORMAL	EMERGENCY	NEUROTIC COPING	NEUROTIC CHARACTER	SEVERE DISORDER
1. ☐				
2. ☐				
	3. ☐			
	4. ☐			
		5. ☐		
		6. ☐		
			7. ☐	
			8. ☐	
				9. ☐
				10. ☐

TICK THE BOXES WHICH CORRESPOND TO YOUR TENSION
BEHAVIOUR. YOUR BEHAVIOUR MAY FALL INTO SEVERAL
STAGES OF MENTAL HEALTH.

DIAGNOSTIC CHART   Characteristic 2: Mood

BEHAVIOUR AND SYMPTOMS

1. Mood swings have cause.
2. Presence of humour.
3. Moods can be intense but pass within short time.

4. Sense of being easily upset, moody, intolerant.
5. Explosive humour as tension release.

6. Moods last for long periods.
7. Intermittent hysterical behaviour.
8. Hyper-emotional expressions without awareness.
9. Hostile wit.
10. Mild chronic fears and phobias.
11. Counterphobic behaviour with some risk.
12. Blocked specific emotions.

13. Background moods affect work, love, play.
14. Chronic depressed, unhappy states.
15. Suicide attempts.
16. Get "high" on ideas but problems in following through.
17. Self-destructive counterphobic acting out.
18. Predictable hysterical behaviour.

19. Delusions, thought disorders, or hallucinations.
20. Severe depression, unreachable, complete halt to work or love.

	NORMAL	EMERGENCY	NEUROTIC COPING	NEUROTIC CHARACTER	SEVERE DISORDER
1.	☐				
2.	☐				
3.	☐				
4.		☐			
5.		☐			
6.			☐		
7.			☐		
8.			☐		
9.			☐		
10.			☐		
11.			☐		
12.			☐		
13.				☐	
14.				☐	
15.				☐	
16.				☐	
17.				☐	
18.				☐	
19.					☐
20.					☐

TICK THE BOXES WHICH CORRESPOND TO YOUR MOOD BEHAVIOUR. YOUR BEHAVIOUR MAY FALL INTO SEVERAL STAGES OF MENTAL HEALTH.

DIAGNOSTIC CHART   Characteristic 3: Thought

Behaviour and Symptoms

1. Able to secure and process information.
2. Thoughts of whatever kind do not upset for long.
3. Thoughts facilitate action.
4. Thoughts intensely, narrowly focused on task or problem.
5. Tension release through thoughts – passive, aggressive, sexual.
6. Selective inattention.
7. Tendency to analyse rather than experience feelings.
8. Questions ability to feel important emotions.
9. Circular worrying.
10. Chronic distortions of reality.
11. Alert to unspecified danger.
12. Deficiency in knowledge.
13. Repetitive, bothersome thoughts disrupt living.
14. Inability to experience specific feelings.
15. Inability to make decisions.
16. Obsessive thoughts.
17. Gross perceptual distortions.

NORMAL	EMERGENCY	NEUROTIC COPING	NEUROTIC CHARACTER	SEVERE DISORDER
1. ☐				
2. ☐				
3. ☐				
	4. ☐			
	5. ☐			
	6. ☐			
		7. ☐		
		8. ☐		
		9. ☐		
			10. ☐	
			11. ☐	
			12. ☐	
			13. ☐	
			14. ☐	
			15. ☐	
				16. ☐
				17. ☐

TICK THE BOXES WHICH CORRESPOND TO YOUR THOUGHT BEHAVIOUR. YOUR BEHAVIOUR MAY FALL INTO SEVERAL STAGES OF MENTAL HEALTH.

DIAGNOSTIC CHART   Characteristic 4: Activity

BEHAVIOUR AND SYMPTOMS

1. Enthusiasm and interest in doing, participating, bringing sense of competence.
2. Risk-taking and resilience — daring to be mediocre or fail and try again.
3. Activity may be uneven or continuous.

4. According to temperament, lots of activity or little.
5. Anxiety about new risks or overload.
6. Talismanic words, behaviour.

7. Hyperactivity with no point.
8. Needs inspiration or feedback to work adequately.
9. Marked reduction in risk-taking.

10. Avoids new activities.
11. Activity no longer relieves tension.
12. Activities solitary, no pleasure in accomplishing, pain if not done.

13. Compulsive ritualistic activity.
14. Extreme difficulty in changing patterns of activity.

| | NEUROTIC | NEUROTIC | SEVERE | |
NORMAL	EMERGENCY	COPING	CHARACTER	DISORDER
1. ☐				
2. ☐				
3. ☐				
	4. ☐			
	5. ☐			
	6. ☐			
		7. ☐		
		8. ☐		
		9. ☐		
			10. ☐	
			11. ☐	
			12. ☐	
				13. ☐
				14. ☐

TICK THE BOXES WHICH CORRESPOND TO YOUR ACTIVITY BEHAVIOUR. YOUR BEHAVIOUR MAY FALL INTO SEVERAL STAGES OF MENTAL HEALTH.

DIAGNOSTIC CHART   Characteristic 5: Organization/Control

Behaviour and Symptoms

1. Can sit still and address self to task for increasingly long periods.
2. Can work in absence of inspiration or feedback.
3. Plan and carry out solutions to multi-step problems.
4. Learn from experience.
5. Freedom to use behavioural repertoire flexibly.

6. Anxiety stimulates action.
7. May lie or cheat under pressure.

8. Increased rigidity: desires clear-cut demands and perfect conditions to function.
9. Chronic condition of being over-extended.
10. Unpredictable events disrupt performance badly.
11. Occasional impulsive behaviour.
12. Rituals interfere with work.
13. Limited capacity for self-generated insight and change.

14. Envies the machine.
15. Unexpected minor events cause work stoppage; ditto in love and play.
16. Obsessive rituals necessary to function.
17. Impulsive behaviour disrupts plans; doesn't learn from experience.

18. Little self-control; easily influenced by suggesion or internal feelings.
19. Feelings dictate when and if work is possible.
20. Impulsive behaviour expected.

	NORMAL	EMERGENCY	NEUROTIC COPING	NEUROTIC CHARACTER	SEVERE DISORDER
1.	☐				
2.	☐				
3.	☐				
4.	☐				
5.	☐				
6.		☐			
7.		☐			
8.			☐		
9.			☐		
10.			☐		
11.			☐		
12.			☐		
13.			☐		
14.				☐	
15.				☐	
16.				☐	
17.				☐	
18.					☐
19.					☐
20.					☐

TICK THE BOXES WHICH CORRESPOND TO YOUR ORGANI-ZATION/CONTROL BEHAVIOUR. YOUR BEHAVIOUR MAY FALL INTO SEVERAL STAGES OF MENTAL HEALTH.

DIAGNOSTIC CHART Characteristic 6: Interpersonal

BEHAVIOUR AND SYMPTOMS

1. Be a friend as well as having friends.
2. Increasing capacity for intimacy.
3. Withdrawal or aggression have clear causes and pass.
4. Can use upset feelings manipulatively to seek attention.
5. Anxiety about pleasing others.
6. Unwillingness or inability to "play".
7. Over-emotional in interpersonal relationships.
8. Irritability.
9. Moving towards, against, or away from others in overdriven manner.
10. Must always get own way, inability to compromise.
11. Can be scapegoated or bullyish.
12. Prematurely initiate one-to-one relationships.
13. Changing, deteriorating friendships often featured by grudges.
14. Need constant external support.
15. Low self-esteem.
16. Mild anti-social behaviour or alienation.
17. Extreme dependency and/or manipulation.
18. Extreme grudges.
19. Autism.
20. Sociopathic behaviour.

	NORMAL	EMERGENCY	NEUROTIC COPING	NEUROTIC CHARACTER	SEVERE DISORDER
1.	☐				
2.	☐				
3.	☐				
4.		☐			
5.		☐			
6.		☐			
7.		☐			
8.		☐			
9.			☐		
10.			☐		
11.			☐		
12.			☐		
13.			☐		
14.			☐		
15.			☐		
16.			☐		
17.				☐	
18.				☐	
19.					☐
20.					☐

TICK THE BOXES WHICH CORRESPOND TO YOUR INTER-PERSONAL BEHAVIOUR. YOUR BEHAVIOUR MAY FALL INTO SEVERAL STAGES OF MENTAL HEALTH.

DIAGNOSTIC CHART   Characteristic 7: Physical

BEHAVIOUR AND SYMPTOMS

1. Stability of GI system, skin, breathing, sleep, weight.
2. Relatively quick recovery from illness/accident.
3. Sense of feeling well.

4. Fluctuations in eating and sleeping patterns, weight, minor GI problems, skin blemishes.
5. Physical sensations of tension, tiredness, of using up physical reserves.
6. Conscious use of drugs to cope.

7. Intermittent skin, GI problems, obesity, lack of appetite, sleep disturbances, headaches.
8. Physical tics, stuttering.
9. Complaints about health with no plainly-defined symptoms.
10. Seeks drugs/medical help to "feel better".
11. Episodic drug abuse, socially reinforced.

12. Stiffness and contraction in physical mannerisms.
13. Chronic psychosomatic problems – ulcers, colitis, insomnia, migraines, absence of periods, anorexia – without clear-cut cause.
14. Chronic solitary drug abuse as coping mechanism or self-medication.
15. Exhaustion.

16. Bizarre physical posturing.
17. Many physical problems.
18. Addictions.

NORMAL	EMERGENCY	NEUROTIC COPING	NEUROTIC CHARACTER	SEVERE DISORDER
1. ☐				
2. ☐				
3. ☐				
	4. ☐			
	5. ☐			
	6. ☐			
		7. ☐		
		8. ☐		
		9. ☐		
		10. ☐		
		11. ☐		
			12. ☐	
			13. ☐	
			14. ☐	
			15. ☐	
				16. ☐
				17. ☐
				18. ☐

TICK THE BOXES WHICH CORRESPOND TO YOUR PHY-SICAL BEHAVIOUR. YOUR BEHAVOUR MAY FALL INTO SEVERAL STAGES OF MENTAL HEALTH.

MENTAL HEALTH
SELF-EVALUATION CHART 2

Calculate your points' score for each characteristic according to the points' allocation table given after that characteristic in the first set of diagnostic charts from page 92. Then shade in the second mental health pictograph opposite. Compare this with the picture of your mental condition which you drew on page 120. If the two pictures differ greatly it is an indication that your mental health has improved or deteriorated. I hope your mental health will have improved because studying this self-evaluation guide is itself therapeutic. Introspection is the base upon which the science of psychology has developed. This book should have helped you to learn about yourself and become aware of tensions and destructive behaviour patterns in everyday life. An improved visual chart is a reflection of the stablizing effect of this heightened awareness.

If your mental condition has deteriorated, do not panic. Minor deterioration may merely reflect increased sensitivity to normal ongoing stress. In many cases, minor mental instability is a sign of needed readjustment which will improve your life in the future. Major deterioration indicates that your environment, physiology and/or life-situation has changed creating new stresses, or that you are being overwhelmed by life's strains and tensions. If this is the case, follow the advice presented in the sections Where Do You Go When You're in Trouble?, Philosophy of Mental Health, Treatment, and the Self-Cure Programme.

SELF-EVALUATION CHART 2

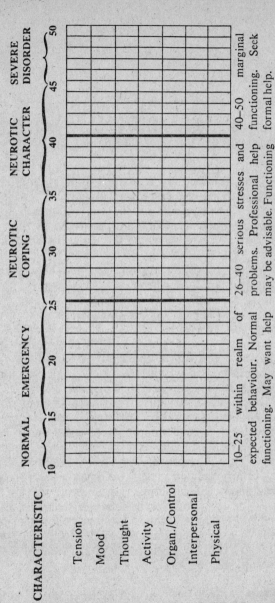

POINTS

CHARACTERISTIC	NORMAL	EMERGENCY	NEUROTIC COPING	NEUROTIC CHARACTER	SEVERE DISORDER
	10 15	20 25	30 35	40	45 50
Tension					
Mood					
Thought					
Activity					
Organ./Control					
Interpersonal					
Physical					

10–25 within realm of expected behaviour. Normal functioning. May want help with specific problems, i.e. preventive therapy.

26–40 serious stresses and problems. Professional help may be advisable. Functioning with difficulty.

40–50 marginal functioning. Seek formal help.

INDEX

OUR PUBLISHING POLICY

HOW WE CHOOSE

Our policy is to consider every deserving manuscript and we can give special editorial help where an author is an authority on his subject but an inexperienced writer. We are rigorously selective in the choice of books we publish. We set the highest standards of editorial quality and accuracy. This means that a *Paperfront* is easy to understand and delightful to read. Where illustrations are necessary to convey points of detail, these are drawn up by a subject specialist artist from our panel.

HOW WE KEEP PRICES LOW

We aim for the big seller. This enables us to order enormous print runs and achieve the lowest price for you. Unfortunately, this means that you will not find in the *Paperfront* list any titles on obscure subjects of minority interest only. These could not be printed in large enough quantities to be sold for the low price at which we offer this series.

We sell almost all our *Paperfronts* at the same unit price. This saves a lot of fiddling about in our clerical departments and helps us to give you world-beating value. Under this system, the longer titles are offered at a price which we believe to be unmatched by any publisher in the world.

OUR DISTRIBUTION SYSTEM

Because of the competitive price, and the rapid turnover, *Paperfronts* are possibly the most profitable line a bookseller can handle. They are stocked by the best bookshops all over the world. It may be that your bookseller has run out of stock of a particular title. If so, he can order more from us at any time – we have a fine reputation for "same day" despatch, and we supply any order, however small (even a single copy), to any bookseller who has an account with us. We prefer you to buy from your bookseller, as this reminds him of the strong underlying public demand for *Paperfronts*. Members of the public who live in remote places, or who are housebound, or whose local bookseller is unco-operative, can order direct from us by post.

FREE

If you would like an up-to-date list of all the paperfront titles currently available, send a stamped self-addressed envelope to
ELLIOT RIGHT WAY BOOKS, BRIGHTON RD.,
LOWER KINGSWOOD, SURREY, U.K.